MW00607140

Do Not
Let Us
Die

Do Not Let Us Die A Book of Revelation

Aniedobe

DoubleCrest

DoubleCrest Publishers, LLC., Bowie, Maryland

ISBN 0-9754133-0-9
LCCN 2004093316

ATTENTION CORPORATIONS, UNIVERSITIES, COLLEGES,
AND PROFESSIONAL ORGANIZATIONS:
Quantity discounts are available on bulk purchases of this book for edu-
cational, gift purposes, or as premiums for increasing magazine sub-
scription or renewals. Special books or book excerpts can also be created to fit specific needs. For information, please contact DoubleCrest
Publishers, LLC. P.O. Box 2340 Bowie, MD 20718: www.DoubleCrest.com.

Dedication

From a long lost brother to the people of the plantations who should not die.

To old black Joe, James, and Mabel, to the lees and plebes among them whose groans of yesteryears filtered into my poetic consciousness.

And for you Willie, whoever you might be, that in these pages you may not die.

And it came to pass

when man began to multiply on the face

of the earth and daughters were born unto them

that the sons of God saw the daughters of men

that they were fair and they took them

wives of all which they choose.

Genesis Chapter 6, Verses 1-2.

Cast of Principal Characters

Agubanze	Second son of Ezenwanmadu.
Author	Direct descendant of Agubanze.
Ebenebe	Farmer. Custodian of the rain forest of Ojita. Agubanze's father in-law.
Euhemerus	Same as Okonkwo by a previous existence.
Ezedumeme	First son of Ezenwanmadu.
Ezenwanmadu	Medicine man, counselor, philosopher. Father of Ezedumeme and Agubanze.
Izaka	One of the errant sons of God. See Genesis, Chapter 6.
Mgbankwocha	Singer, dancer and historian.
Nwabuno	Griot and oral historian. Ex-wife of Nwoye.
Nwanyiekie	Izaka's favorite lover. Reputed as the prettiest woman that ever lived.
Nwoye	Palm wine tapster, connoisseur and philosopher. Best friends with Ezenwanmadu. Briefly married to Nwabuno.
Okonkwo	Drummer, poet, oral historian. Reincarnated as Euhemerus.
Willie Johnson	African-American. Died in the Vietnam war. Still missing in action.

Contents

Preface

My generation is probably the first of fully culturally assimilated sub-Saharan Africans who naively laid a friendly arm on the white man's shoulder, and was disappointed that he rudely shrugged it off and flung it back into the middle of the previous century. We were then faced with the onerous task of extricating Western cultural influences from our authentic African roots.

Nowhere is an African more apt to feel betrayed than in America. In struggling to re-affirm ourselves, we ultimately realize that both the victim and the victimizer are faced with a terrible sense of loss. It is my opinion that a black man may cry victim only to the extent that he may take stock of his losses, when he loses the zeal for contributive citizenship, he has become a victim solely of himself. He must look despair in the eye, mock it, traverse that canyon of self-disaffirmation and come out undiminished and irreducible; the burden being as great as the reward.

The verses you are about to read came upon me, and were triggered by circumstances not unconnected with my struggles against racial discrimination. Accordingly, the main narrative thrust of this book is the African-American experience told from the unique perspective of an African suddenly immersed into the American society. However snugly aligned with the narrative are embodiments that are philosophical, theological, metaphysical, and anthropological; for the verses, written as I was told to write, convey actual manifestations that I witnessed over a three year span.

As a philosophical work, it is a scholarly and afrocentric exploration of the nature of man and God, by analyzing the theory of truth and the genesis of classes, to the asserted end that there would be classes as long as there are men. What however, must be preached is heightened sensitivity based on the realization that what affects one will ultimately affect the other. As an anthropological work, it is a Euhemerist story of an African people of a bygone era, of cultural innocence, replete with myth, heroes, and human intrigues. Above all, it is a spiritual odyssey that adopts an interesting, if apocalyptic, prophetic hue.

In terms of style, this book is written entirely in the dramatic poetry of the talking drum; its unique dialectic derivative of the oral culture of the great Igbo people of present day Eastern Nigeria. The Igbos prior to the 1890's were very flowery in speech, employed rhetoric and cadence with great deliberation, and provided a sense of spiritual harmony with their environment. Among them, the beauty of words must be unobtrusively explored. This was the cornerstone of their linguistic culture. Although, there have been in several other works, glimpses of how the Igbos spoke, never before have their poetics been this unabashedly presented.

The drum talks in Igbo land—often canorously and with poetic sparsity, and a logorrhic drum may be sent back to the forest. This book is written to the accompaniment of the drum, which follows, affirms and concurs, while the poet leads. I should also point out for the benefit of my Western Audience that tone is organic to sub-Saharan languages. There is no amount of translational skill that could be brought to bear to carry across the *organotope*, the full extent of the vibrancy and innate stimuli of the oral genre. I share in the belief that any medium of expression, like spring, may be stretched or compressed; like fluid, may be condensed or dispersed; like dough, may be pounded into any form or pattern. Whatever may be done to language must be done, as is necessary to bear an adequate and efficient burden of the gamut of a people's cultural experiences.

English language in particular, must bear the burden of its universalization, as may involve cumulative distortion, obsolescence, death, and a refreshing rebirth among cultures on which it has been imposed. That said, I ignored the tedium of rhymes and meters in hope for an easy read and yet literary rigor, sometimes taut, sometimes slack, and sometimes abstruse, and yet crafted for universal appeal. And for effect, it is my sincere hope that your own will to love be not strained.

Introduction

Do Not Let Us Die starts off with I, the bandleader and the lead dancer, inviting the reader to join me in an incredible dance at the end of which I shall tell him/her why the caged bird sings. The singing caged bird is used allegorically to refer to why I must write these verses in spite of circumstances, at the time of their writing, which precluded indulgence in the flowery and the aesthetic.

Then in the second Chapter entitled "Song Of Myself," I introduce the reader to my own worldview. However, the true story begins with a wintry night in Connecticut when I plunged into a deep meditation in the third Chapter entitled "Song of my God" and continues with the spiritual odyssey that ensued in the "Voices," culminating in a most incredible vision of a young man in Harlem called "Willie Johnson." Willie, according to him, died in Vietnam. He was a young black man who, it appears, did not understand why he had to go and fight and die. And so, Willie actually appeared to me, narrated stories about his family, and begged me to "not let us die." It was actually Willie's bidding that led me to relocate from Connecticut to Georgia, for Willie had said, "While in Georgia, feel the earth, red with their blood."

Disturbed by Willie's revelation, I plunged back into more meditation in the Chapter entitled "Song Of The Fountain" resulting in another spiritual encounter, this time with the lamentations of Nwabuno—a legendary poet and griot, in the Chapter entitled "Footsteps On The Anthill." Nwabuno would later play a leading role in the narrative. My companion and spiritual guide was Okonkwo/Euhemerus. He was also the drummer to whose accompaniment all of the songs were written.

Now, the real story begins with the visitation of three Patriarchal figures: Ezenwammadu, Ebenebe and Nwoye. The Chapter entitled "The First Encounter" captures my first meeting with them. You could call them spiritual guides. They were extremely solicitous of my welfare and I remain grateful to them. Of the three of them, Nwoye was the funniest and most remarkable. Nwoye was briefly married to Nwabuno— mentioned above, and their verbal sparring filled me with lots of laughter. Nwoye has no single serious "bone" in him, in the sense that his carefree attitude was quite palpable. We both engaged in verbal sparring of our own. Ezenwanmadu, the other Patriarchal fellow was the firmer and more serious. He was their leader and he knew a lot to put it mildly. You had the sense that his patriarchal machinations brought all this about. Ebenebe, on the other hand, was the more conciliatory and circumspect of the three. The connection there is that Ezenwanmadu's second son, Agubanze, of whom I am a direct descendant, was married to Ebenebe's daughter. That is why Ezenwanmadu would affectionately call me "Son of his father" and Ebenebe would call me "Son of his mother." Nwoye, on the other hand was best friends with Ezenwanmadu. Funny enough, you get the feeling that Nwoye and Ezenwanmadu were as different as can be.

The next two Chapters "Thoughts So Far Strayed" and "The Will To Love Is Not Strained" detail some of what transpired in their subsequent visitations. In those Chapters, the reader is told about my internal wrangling with racial prejudices and how the mystery fellows—or the Patriarchs helped me to re-affirm myself. They would subsequently transport me with them in "Before Ham We Were" to an amazing encounter captured in "People Of Paradise." Here Nwabuno re-emerges to tell the story of the ancient people of Nimo in present day Eastern Nigeria and of Izaka. Izaka was one of the errant sons of God, or so it seems, mentioned in the book of Genesis who dwelt with, lorded, and terrorized the people of Nimo. According to the story, both Agubanze and Nwabuno died at the hands of Izaka. Nwabuno, you might say, was the people's chief prosecutor. In the Chapter entitled "Song Of Izaka" you will find the trial of this fellow whom I suspect was probably more than the patriarchs were letting on. Anyway, the trial of Izaka was the last event I witnessed in Connecticut before I followed Willie's bidding and moved to Georgia.

Two significant events happened in Atlanta, Georgia. It was in Atlanta that the mystery fellows stopped by for the last time to say goodbye in "A Child's Wellspring Of Gratitude" and in the final Chapter entitled "One More Song To Sing," I bid an emotional farewell to my spiritual companion, Okonkwo. The other major event was the apparition of the petit lady, our lady, clad in brilliant white, complexioned of sunlight, and more magnificent than an array of stars. Neither words nor the imagination can do justice to her beauty, which paled in comparison to the kindness she evokes. She instructed that I write what I had seen and heard and so I did.

Chapter 1

A Story I Tell

Soon will peace settle
On the agitator's mind
And all his aghastness
Shall not have been for naught.
Soon will the wind of awakening
Caress our toddling minds.

Not like Eliot, Pound, or Soyinka,
Of me and mine, variegated,
Influenced and influential,
A story I tell …
Of anguished howls, from this émigré,
At the boundary born
Of the past and the present,
From the present that wearies me,
A glimpse into a past unbeknownst,
And encumbered by the yoke of time,
The future, imposed upon me.

Pregnant *is the present with the future,*
Of its fate, there is no telling.
Yet if she must insist that her young
Would not a snake be,
The expectant mother-snake would be made
To show the product of her travail.

We chew sticks that the jaws may dance.
With proverbs, our palm oil, we eat our words.
Let he who would restrain our dancing steps,
Not look back upon setting out.

Here is a story by one who says:
'The eye that looks down will
Surely see its nose.
A foraging mind picks up dirt,
Its freedom is quickly usurped.
The finger that scratches
Will be laden with flakes of flesh.
And he that must exhume history reposed,
Let him not tire out.
And he that tugs at the veil
That covers the unknown,
Let him be prepared for unpleasant disclosures.
For the overzealous scratching hen
Sometimes unearths what might kill it.

Beware! The hen that rushes
In wild pursuit of the lizard often
Runs into the wall.
The blacksmith who cannot make gongs
Is advised to study the tail of the hawk,
And the monkey that must swallow whole fruits
Should first size up its anus.

The fast moving legs will be seen
By the fast seeing eyes.
The eyes that do not see
Shall see things that are not seen.
The ear that does not hear
Shall hear things that are not heard.
Those who rake up
Layers of history reposed,
Beware, lest you get trapped in the past.
And yet, those who follow
The unknown past up to the extent
That it goes, come to the present
For all there is, has been.

The thrills of discovery
May as yet be dampened by the
Anxiety over its aftermath.
But hold unto me and be patient
And I will tell you a story like no other.

An only stomach does not rush upon a tasty soup
It soon swells and aches.[1]
And so, do not rush upon this story
So that your stomach may not swell or ache.

Euhemerus,[2] do they not associate in pairs,
Guinea fowls, who insist
On an extra pair of sentry's eyes?
Come, as a dear friend would,
Let us take this painful walk.

In the back roads of history,
Upon its broad shoulder paths,
Let us take this walk.
Do not scamper away, soul brother,
For we are not afraid of the road
Upon which we were thrust,
By which thereby we came.
Do not excuse of our scant accoutrements
But come, let us rejoice in
The dereliction of the back roads.

Arm in arm,
Let us skip down its alleyway.
With pure heart and the abandon
Of a mindless free bird, let us soak
In its effusive primordiality.
Upon seeing the bones of our ancestors
Strewn far afield, let us with
Reverent gestures salute their memories.
Upon its ageless trees and dry reeds
Let us bestow a solemn benignity.
And of the dusts that have
Settled upon its pebbles,
Let us not even a grain awaken.

Instead, like dew upon grass
Dwellers at dawn, let its
Memories settle in our minds.
We, who must justify the present
So that it may proudly
Dwell with the past.
We, who were born of
The wisdom of the past,
The suffusive light,
The silent hortator that urges,
'Glorify the present,
Celebrate the past,
For soon will one fuse into the other

And your efforts strewn upon the present
Shall form the ever-growing landscape
Of the back roads of history.'

Soon will peace settle
On the agitator's mind
And all his aghastness
Shall not have been for naught.
Soon will the wind of awakening
Caress our toddling minds.
Then at twilight, we will say,
'A tower indeed, of numerous tongues,
That enlightened all, that depleted itself.'
For one would say, 'amazing,
That which I felt, magnificent indeed.'

And another would say, 'more amazing,
More magnificent, indeed, only I
Did the truth truly feel.'
Thus, the wisdom which they
Have attained embellishes one,
Yet sets him up in a
Perpetual motion of grief and discord.

Euhemerus, look beyond the horizon,
Are there not other raconteurs,
That gather slowly like puddles
To witness history that creeps past,
Sometimes that whirls past,
Sometimes in solemn procession past,
And still beyond the horizon,
Do we not hear strange dirges,
Songs of maidens lost,
Devil's mirage, prowler of the prowler,
Turn not back, time and truth urge us.

We will skip arm in arm.
We will behold the same sights.

We will carouse together,
Drunk in our vision.
We will be friends forever,
United in common knowledge.

To those that ask, 'What have you felt?'
We will answer, 'that which is
Not for philosophical midgets.'
To those that ask, 'What medium?'
We will answer, 'the elaborate poetics
Of the tribes of the rain forest,
To an untrained mind, unorthodox or
Avant garde, certainly to a Westerner,
To an African, a nostalgic revisitation.'
To those that ask, 'What purpose?'
We will most certainly say,
'An attempt at *verigraphy* -
An analysis of the sociology of truth.'
And to those that ask, 'What attitude?'
We will say, 'unaffected, impolitic,
Yet heartfelt and humanistic.'

And if we are asked,
'Verse makers, where lies your gratitude?'
We will most certainly say,
'To Paul Bell[3], to Michael Cutlip[4]
To Alyssa, Kunle, Elias and Martina
And to the petite lady of perfect proportions,
Who is fairer than the moon,
Brighter than a thousand suns, and
More magnificent than a procession of stars;
And to him, of course, who must be feared.'

And if we have been
Entertaining in the process,
We will drink again to ourselves,
And again and again, until
We hear the raucousness

Of the men of violence in us,
Then we will part company, proselytizing …
As we totter, burdened by knowledge,
Down the road of time.

Drumbeat! Drumbeat!

'That the yam tuber is big is true
That it cannot be harvested is false.[5]
The man who insists on finding
What is not in the market place will
Consort with the vultures.[6]
Be cheerful and of good courage
For the tortoise fell into the trench
And declared that all land is truly land.
'For,' says the vulture,
'As certain as tomorrow
Is the death of another weary animal.'

'It is not always the case that an open eye sees …
Still, one who does not contemplate the future dwells in the past…
But do not pour sand on yesterday until you have seen what tomorrow
brings.'

Endnotes

[1] It is considered rude among the Igbos to eat alone unless one has made a good faith effort to ask others to join you and they decline.

[2] Euhemerus, the drummer-poet is also called Okonkwo. The italicized verses are the sayings of Euhemerus.

[3] Professor of Chemical Engineering, University of Connecticut, Storrs, CT.

[4] Professor of Chemical Engineering, University of Connecticut, Storrs, CT.

[5] A big yam tuber is highly prized among the Igbos. Harvesting it is only a minor inconvenience.

[6] Vultures are a common feature of the open marketplace typical of Sub-Saharan Africa. They are generally seen around abattoirs and in any case, freely roaming the empty market place.

Chapter 2

Song Of Myself

I will make a bold and loud
Celebration of my blackness
And dance bare-buttocked
With infectious pride,
In bemused crotch-clutching engaged,
And remain through all bewildering
Beholden to my Africaness.

Sprawled before the noonday sun,
Immense, mountainous,
That cannot be tethered,
In all its raw vintage,
Is my passion spilled...
And you poets, prophets, and proselytes
You will testify that I speak of
That which must be spoken.

M*y songs are my bearers,*
They immortalize me.
By them, I am carried
Wherever I am carried.
Listen, chest thumpers
Who gaze with upward pride,
Declare to me and I shall listen,
If you hear the voice of the
Howling wind or understand the
Hiding place of its storehouses.
Would you then blame me.
If I desire only the company
Of he who tells me all things?

Despise me, if you must
To whatever extent you may, despise me
Indeed assume if you may, what you may...
Still, I proclaim you a starry spot
In the vast nebula of my mind.
I am on your side, your tribune,
Your vanguard, for you, your idolater...
Infantile, geriatric, straight laced,
Whatever character you assume,
Whatever tenor or timber,
Whatever anatomical garb or comportment,
Whatever state of mind or body,
Whatever class you arrogate or are assigned,
Whatever plume of skin,
Whatever clime you dwell,

I will be genuinely amused.

You are the yam tubers
To my fertile swamp...
I am the asker,
The overly curious child,
I will never get lost…
I present questions, not answers,
I am that earnest seeker of a thousand receptacles
Primed to accept a tithe of your own genius.
I will ask you, and you will respond
To me and to my universe
For the sole benefit of my passionate arousal
That hope may continually be spawned.

W*ould the chicken that has not scratched*
Look forward to the feast of ants?
Come, let our good efforts precede our reward.
Of the rhythm that falls before us,
Let us dance.

Come, meet Nwoye whose stomach
Grows not weary of a good palm wine,
Whose legs tire not after good music,
Who advises that if a hill becomes strenuous
We must learn to rest between climbs.

Let he who admires the shed skin of a molting snake
Also admire the stick that bears it.
Meet Euhemerus, the drummer-poet
Of a thousand different beats
Sometimes terse as the tightest poetry
Sometimes slack as children's prose
Sometimes abstruse as the visions of a mad man.
He was often known to say that
He was like a toad, who does not know how else
To cry, without the in-rush of water to its mouth.

Come, we will dance
Of the rhythm that falls before us,
Let us dance.

Let the adult who dances with children
Not complain if he is out-danced.
And let those who cannot dance find an excuse.
If you were once a dancer, tell us,
'The story teller whose well of inspiration dried up,
Says the children of the tortoise have all grown up,'
And if you have never danced before, tell us,
'The chicken says that pregnancy is best left
For those who have legs.'
The tree that refuses to dance will be taught by the wind.
And if you must dance alone, set out early
And elect the night, where bad dancers excel.

Come, the snail moves with its shell.
All that are itching to dance, come.
The penis that survives death
Eats the bearded meat.
Come, today is the day after the day of death.
Come, bread fruit to my palm kernel
Let us meet at my chin,
For itching men scratch one another,
Animals employ the aid of the tree trunk.

Come, make songs with me.
Like grass, let us bathe of the water we fetch.
For today it will rain,
And the quarrelers will disperse,
And nothing shall have been lost.
The rain that may spoil our journey
Will not restrain our dancing steps.

We will be as cavalier as the bearded vulture
Who insists that the mere fact of her pregnancy
Is already a gain, for in the event of a miscarriage

She will eat both her fetus and the grass cutter.

Let the dancing crab beware of its terrain
And the weak-headed chicken
Refrain from the brawl of the woodpeckers…
But the exuberant bird flies past its nest,
Therefore, let commonsense temper your zeal,
For aloofness is the snake's undoing.
A person who falls in dance
Is remembered more than the dance itself.
The palm kernel eater does not make a pendant
Of his cracking stone.
Rather than drown fully clothed,
Let us gladly release our loincloth to the raging river.

Come, stand not around.
He who watches a dwarf
Merely shows himself to the dwarf.
Come, dull is a ceremony without us.
Color is prettiest when by us, pythons,
It is most elegantly worn.
Fall behind me, and I will teach you
The unique steps of the randy he-goat
Whose techniques were perfected at his grandmother's.
Fall behind me, and I will teach you
Why he who dances to every tune
Soon becomes lame on both legs.

Drumbeat! Drumbeat!

'We do not express laughter the way a person is tickled …
The jaws might break.'

If you need me now, look for me.
I am the lonely mad man of your neigborhood,
I work the littered landscape of souls.
Among that heap of discarded rubbery,
Open balls of half-truths,

There, the festival ground,
I will ask you to celebrate our humanity.

Drumbeat! Drumbeat!

I acknowledge nothing, but nothing itself.
I denounce everything that is *discompetent*,[1]
The slush of hatred in which men are mired.
I denounce hatred, covert, overt,
Insidiously destroying, in every format,
And the dearth of pure and undiluted joy...

I welcome the company of the wicked
More than the fool's besotting
For nothing bothers me more than
The arrogance of a fool,
His strange imperatives,
His contorted outlook ...
And then, the incomprehension of myself,
The instinctive, illogical, *circumprogressive*[2]
Motions of my existence - and yet
As often as I could, I serenade my amazing self.

I amaze myself.
At the giddy heights of my wisdom,
And the dizzying depths of my foolishness,
Starry is my wide unbelief.

I trivialize everything.
Finding mockery and laughter in all things
As I nullify myself, and today,
And tomorrow, and today...
Becoming nothing as all becomes nothing...
Becoming all as all becomes me,
Then merging with all things,
I make inquiries to its surfeit.
Yet on my best days, I feel like
A Parkinsonian fumbler in the dark.

My life is still strange to me.
Sometimes, it is like a drama
Written by a superlative fool
Upon which is inadvertently sprinkled,
Traces of superb craftsmanship.
What with viperous men
Upon whose *discompetence*
Best efforts are spilled
And mediocrity condoned
In the face of conformity.
At their ineptitude,
At their blatant deeds of hate,
I took great umbrage…
Although they provoked poetry
And sent creative impulses
Arching all over me.

Waves crashing upon waves,
Ripples billowing through ripples,
Deep furrows and grooves,
Dark geological schisms,
Fiery vituperations…
Internalizing all of them,
I wooed peace scarcely restored.
Threadbare, ill-clad, without a home,
In humble communion I craved,
As I ran upon an irregular terrain
Of brash and defiance,
Making verses of myself
Turgid with emotions
Resolved at all times, to be
Potent, progressive and irreducible.

See the anger of clenched fists,
The resentment that habits within,
Following that grasping for breath
That dimming of the eyes
That staggering of legs and

That contented smile hung between the teeth
And a mental tom-tom
Voice of the inner spirit that says,
'You have won,'
And yet you were not duly acknowledged.

The cream always rise,
Given enough stretch of work.
The cream will float on top
Given that the stirrer will stop stirring.

Euhemerus, the queen's breath
Soon turns too much sulfide for my admiration.
For when I look at her retinue of admirers,
I also think of her crises, alone,
While making a toilet.
For is it any secret, your majesty,
That those who eat good food,
Make the smelliest feces?
Or is your majesty's anus catheterized
To avoid any olfactory difficulties?

Welcome to my world, one without taboos,
Unsurpassingly beautiful,
Indiscriminately to be enjoyed.
Like the termite,
I have no waist for fancy clothes.
I celebrate beauty that is elementary
And not upkept with empty pride
And adore nature as best I can...
For what beauty is there that can match:

The glory of the August wind,
The dropping of sap in the rain forest,
The discordant cries of a thousand weaverbirds,
The outcoming of nocturnal animals,
The grace of an eagle riding the hazard
Of the gale wind,

The fury of hurricane,
The smell of the armpit of the African Manatee,
The short-lived thrill of orgasmic eruptions,
The leery eyes of the crocodiles,
The perennial courtship of fawning hens,
And the labor of long-billed birds…
All nature's pulses at full blast.

What beauty is there that can match:
The astringent drip of sweat,
The sweaty brow of the construction worker,
The callused hands of the assembly line worker,
The blistered palm of the tiller
The aching back of the immigrant fruit picker,
The tired legs of the janitor,
The sleepy eyes of the third shift cashier,
And the struggles of other workers,
All of whom, in good labor, join
To denounce the dictatorship of interest groups?

Welcome to this unrehearsed drama, welcome!
A job that was never begun is never ended,
Welcome, make haste to merge with me.
The lizard would have grown hairs but for procrastination.
Welcome, this story is about the pottery
That spilled the water intent upon shattering it.
Welcome, your duty is to watch as I amend
This pottery cracked in many places,
For where once there was fire,
Now there are only ashes.
Welcome, all joyfully,
Your joy will form the fabric of this bounteous light -
This rubious glow of my immortal self.

Welcome to my world…
One without taboos
Unsurpassingly beautiful
Indiscriminately to be enjoyed…

Welcome to my enigmatic world…
Welcome to this city built
Upon a trash heap of information.

My world descried is a poetry,
Immathematical,[3] unrhymed, and sweet,
Completely and utterly sensuous.
Every motion I perceive,
Every thought I perform,
Every thing I vouchsafe to admire,
Becomes a fodder for my arousal…
Then, I recline and tug at he
That hardly beholds the sun,
In frenzied query, feeling those harbingers
Of life and death, maniacal impulses…
They alone witnesses my soulful smiles
As at the moment when heaven begins to merge with me,
Hobbling on a broken limb.

Welcome to my enigmatic world,
Welcome to this city built
Upon a trash heap of information.
If I urge listen, you will listen.
But listening has its responsibilities,
For knowing all that I know
Compels you to act as I might.

Drumbeat! Drumbeat!

Put your ears to the ground,
Hear the songs of the ants.
I am the dancing wayfarer,
If you listen carefully,
You will hear my drummer in the nearby bush.

I will make a bold and loud
Celebration of my blackness
And dance bare-buttocked

With infectious pride,
In bemused crotch-clutching engaged,
And remain through all bewildering
Beholden to my Africaness.

I am a poet, protean and incisive,
Of toleration, equally of black and white,
And universal brotherhood...
Eat of my morsel, for today,
I hold forth verses that cleanse...
And you will indeed learn why the caged bird sings.

I have fallen a thousand times
Yet in all my efforts, I delight.
Both fruitful and futile,
They challenge me to avoid
The tragedy of not having tried.
Ask me not of the medals of triumph,
Instead, ask me of how gallantly
I have fought. For today shares my dreams,
My struggles, mortalizes me,
And the sole purpose of tomorrow
Is to await my certain rebirth.

If you are taller than I am,
Realize that I am proudly shorter than you are.
Let each pilgrim to their reflections,
Each religious to their attitudes.
I am myself, an experiencer,
Prone at times to immoderation...
I look, I listen, I learn,
I seek out occasions to let out a laugh.
For what is there that cannot be done with ease
When all there is to do is to laugh aloud?

From impossible to improbable to inevitable,
So everything yields when
Challenged with a good dose of laughter.

If you would but feel the joy of
Self-mockery and abandonment,
The therapy of self-nullification,
The thrill of the leveler's art,
And the harmony of heartfelt laughter.

I command you today to
Let heartfelt laughter be your religion
And happiness, that monument to laughter,
Be the temple of your soul.

I carry a large one
Of that which everyone carries;
The mind, tote bag of life's experiences,
And I embody numerous consciousnesses…
The indolent, the industrious,
The Mapuche, the Europeans,
The King, the commoner,
The workers – blue or white-collared,
The child, the adult,
The nun, the prostitute,
The artist, the scientist,
The politician and the priest;
They interest and affect me all the same.

Although no less a monger than a monger,
Do not issues take with me.
For being not of any ideological bent,
But a slave, this I am,
To overriding impulses of versification…
Hence I sing of that which must be sung.
For I will tell the king if I am told,
But will decline to bring him, if I am asked.

Drumbeat! Drumbeat!

And thence shall I arise
And return to my father.

All my competition is against me
But win, I seldom do.
My complaints are long, loud and clear
And my cheering no less the same.
I salute men mindful of good
And strive the just to do.
But then, I look up to me and me alone
And not even to Chief Malone.[4]

I whistle and sing and clap and run
And take pleasure when I can
But languish in thoughts, oft I do
As I try to sort the world.

Now you see how droll to rhyme
Except when to stymie, we deign.
The driveling as of infants young,
Being no pleasure to the strong.
Now, we must spur along
For the vistas far are flung.

Drumbeat! Drumbeat!

M*any are the stops of the mad man*
Not to mention his dances in between.
But do not presume that the housefly is dancing
Merely because it is disposing off waste matter.

I love my poetry lying down,
Working my limbs like a purring cat,
Letting frames of images drift idly by.
For indeed, behold with me:
The flight of vanquished soldiers,
The swearing of the soothsayer
When pressed to tell a lie,
The gory handiwork of the assassin,
The gathering of men at the decedent's bedside

The widows cry!

The beat of the gong, *abia* dancers, the eulogy
The apprehensive laughter of the widow, her halitosis
The widow's cry!

Drumbeat! Drumbeat!

The buried corpse acknowledges the flutist,
The sand restrains his dancing steps.
The sick man cries,
He mocks the foolery of the dead;
The dead that easily surfeit of sleep.

Behold with me:
The nostalgia of arthritic limbs on moonlit nights,
The uneasiness of the poor man,
His preoccupation with dreams of wealth,
The trepid steps of the dancer on borrowed costumes,
The bad dancer, his struggles with his body,
The discomfiture of his relatives,
The bird on the fence,
The fence on its legs,
The widow's cry!

Ah, the ease of leisure,
The chagrin of loss,
The drifting of idle thoughts,
The loose acknowledging of self,
The brokered laughter of the boss,
The agony of privation,
The torpor of the prostitute,
The mirthless grin of the white woman…
A twenty-five cents gratuity…
The rejoicing of toothless girls
At the sight of a pizza pie…
The escapist smile of the teenage girl,
The deftness of a tongue uttering languages,

The skill of the flute player,
His strength, his fingers,
The trembling of his lips,
The fool's upbeat, his uneven tempo,
His distorted outlook, the widow's cry!

The baby's outstretched hands,
Her cancer-ridden mother,
The idle hands of the drug addict,
The frozen homeless black man on main street,
The widow's cry!

Drumbeat! Drumbeat!

Behold with me:
The herding of men,
The regimentation of ideas,
The Klansman behind the bench, peevish,
His tainted garble,
Justice hurriedly dispensed in colors…
The lines on the old woman's face,
The stories that time told,
The efforts of the cripple,
Thoughts of thalidomide drifting by…
A dead woman, a stolen baby,
New tears to cry, the widow's cry!

I make no claims to discovery,
An apostle, not of any style or creed.
Unitarian, roundly organic, I,
Urger unto drowsy ears, I plead,
My abjuration of rigorism, preferring
That kernels be sifted from their husks.

I have heard it sometimes advised,
To a full legged man,
To neither walk nor run…
Raise fingers, dare, I say,

If they fit, pick your stuffy nose
And claim not the mannerisms of
Any breeders of false etiquettes.
For no matter how large they are,
The fingers, tips of a man,
Will always be smaller
Than the opening of his nose.

Support, I urge, your head,
With whatever hand that pleases you.
And any man who has nowhere to place
His hands may freely rest them on his knees.

No iconoclast am I,
I am he, otherwise, without definition,
Resisting titles, desiring
To be spared from dysfunctionalism[5]
And men's company who bandy false pride.

I am like the unruly river that breaks its banks.
I hold boundaries to great distaste.
Indeed, freedom and I are like two comrades
Alike as one hand is to another, warriors both,
When we posture in fight, all of repression cringes.

At the confluence of freedom and I,
At the union of our great *homoselves*,[6]
Stand I, a bloodied warrior of many battles,
Pleading, 'Do not die O freedom.
Do not abandon me O able companion.
For out of the fortresses of slavery have arisen
The fortresses of neoslavery accommodation
And they too must fall. O freedom,
O shoddy, disfigured and undervalued one,
Be you the substratum of my visions
A tributary, surpassing the main.'

I make no apologies for who I am,
Although sometimes appalled by what I am,
A predator, left to the contrivances of my hungry soul.
But still I declare that I am a man,
In all its epitome, I am,
Tongue-tied with common humanity,
A spelunker, through thoughts trapped in caves sublime,
Seek a whiff of life to give,
To birth, still, black or white,
A ransom for the agony of loneliness twined around me.

Euhemerus, I internalized all of them,
Trauma after trauma…
Blisters unto blisters…
Fluxes swirling into fluxes…
Tartaric and denigrative remarks…
Eliciting omnivariant impulses
And poetic hysteria…
And burnished by those cataclysmic influences
And without apologies to any sense of orderedness,
I submit this song of my proud and black self.

The world owes not the black man.
Cry freedom, he may, that history's
Verities must be known.
For history unheeded relives itself.
True upon the blackman was wrought
An unpardonable evil, but still
He may not cry victim
And let loose, the ill wind of hate…

As rain pours on good and disaffected soil alike,
On both the slave's and his master's
Let your love, like rain,
Pour on every housetop.
Let its relentless outpouring
Take deep root, moisten all souls,
And bring forth a fresh out-blooming of human dignity.

Drumbeat! Drumbeat!

Like a creeping plant
Is the affection of a good man…
It knows no boundaries.

Black man of the inner city
By any means necessary, move on.
Let the one-handed carry the one-legged,
For the earthworm burrows with its stomach.
By any means necessary, move on.
The two-legged termite sets out before its fellows.
The swift-footed animal may make
A bold burst for freedom,
And its slow-footed counterpart
Must await an auspicious time.

By any means necessary, move on.
For to be dead and free is more fruitful than
To be alive in perpetual bondage…
If men die, men will die.
If they should, let men die.
Only cowards wish that others
Die their deaths.

Son of my kind mother,
Do not give me another excuse
Of your long-running miseducation.
Is water fetched with a basket?
Should the slave not listen and learn
When the son of the household is being taught?

You that grew up on the streets,
You, son of my kind mother,
You, my beloved nigger, stop.
Stop! Fight and die.

Black man of the inner city,
Would you insist on being a toad
That regales in a shallow cesspool?
You of the fabled story past
May you die well.
Better in dignity, to die, free
Than to live bound by
Grossly diluted spirituality.

Black man of the suburb,
A slave does not lick his lips
While pounding his master's yam.
Have you not heard that the slave
Who rejoices at the burial of a fellow slave,
Mocks his impending death?
Or have you not heard that a debtor is a slave?
Or that a caged bird grows not fat?
Need the eye be told of its affiliation with the nose?
Would what affect one not affect the other?
You of the suburb are the festoons,
He of the inner-city is the house,
And a house is not known to fall without its festoons.

Take issues, if you must, with Euhemerus and me.
We are stones cast upwards,
You are the pieces of pottery that must tremble.
Does a single sane man pursue a lizard?
Is it not when urine is made together that it foams?
Those who admire the shape of a face,
Let them not ignore the back of the head
Upon which it is constructed.

Drumbeat! Drumbeat!

The crackhead has run out,
Desperation is bodied all over him.
The girl in the *hood*
Covered her pregnancy with her hands

Until it grew unwieldy
And her agony multiplied.
The subteen grows chesty,
He wonders if he could lift the ground.
The teenage boy sees his erection,
He challenges his god to a wrestling match.
The teenage girl sees her breasts,
She smells advances,
She says, 'not yet prom nite.'

The Jewish boy is told,
'There is no place like Zion.'
Yet Zion lies naked in the sun
Smoldering in ruin, ash unto ash,
And her overturned stones are bathed
By the tears of people far away.
'Holy was the city of Zion
God dwelt within its gates,
In all things stay Jewish.
Moses will come again
And lead us back to Zion.'

Even as man pursues a shadow
So does he await Jerusalem on the hill
In the territory of the Jebusites.
Jerusalem dwells in the hearts of gentiles
The Children of Jacob yell blasphemy!
And John smiles from heaven's playground.
Among the gentiles, prophets are raised
Even like Mohammed, the son of Ishmael.

Drumbeat! Drumbeat!

The mob has overwhelmed the police.
The policemen must run for their lives.
The Chief has gone to a fundraiser.
Angry passions are loosened on the streets.
Sirens! Barking dogs! Anonymity of the mob!

Frigorific breeze of the wind of revolutionary change!
Appeals for calm! The status quo is good!
'The future shall be greater than the past
If only you remain calm,'
The President has spoken.
'So long as minorities burn their neighborhoods
The inner-cities must be white-washed.'
'We must be tough on crime,
Mandatory sentences is constitutionally tight,'
The VP says from the golf course.
'Give us your money. We must be tough on blacks,
One more good justice and the fourth amendment
Will be right where it ought to be.'
A conservative speaks at the country club
'The liberals are soft on blacks,
This is the cornerstone of our campaign.'
Mr. President says again.

Ah, anger transforms oratory
And makes champions of spineless men.
True, the world is ruled on guts alone,
Sometimes that much will do,
But men are hungry, very hungry, you see
And a lot more guts are strained.

Drumbeat! Drumbeat!

See as the Lord's grip tightens
The church frowns, and the churchgoers laugh.
'The priest is gay and he will abuse a child today
How dare he frown at us.'
Again the churchgoers let loose another uproar,
As the cumulus cloud begins
To assume the fingers of a storm.
And the poet, he that must be heeded says,
'His fury is like the madness
Of a male thunder,
And the gathering of ten million angry men

Is to him like the gathering of
Ten million ants, with one breath
Of fire, he consumes them all.'

Drumbeat! Drumbeat!

L*et boils not erupt on the lips*
Of the flute player,
He who is accustomed to wiping a runny nose.
The deaf man who claims,
He has not heard about the dry season
Does he also not feel the cold?
The cold of the dry season
Whose mornings are best met by the fireside.
When we tell a story that interests a bed-ridden man
Let us help him up,
For the dance has just begun,
The antelopes are already breaking their legs.
When this sleep begins to taste good,
We will begin to snore.
Still, let laughter not assume it is a wrestler
Because we sometimes fall for it.

Endnotes

[1] An otherwise competent person who is placed in a ill-suited position.

[2] Progression that is both linear and cyclical.

[3] A system that cannot be adequately represented in any arbitrary state space.

[4] Chief Malone has only stylistic relevance, serving to illustrate the bondage of rhymes and meters.

[5] The trait of being motivated in an extreme sort of way.

[6] Meaning alike as to self and personality.

Chapter 3

Song Of My God

Joy ineffable, amazing delight,
The thrill of a soul in upward flight,
The fusion of man and God
One light to one light, journey's end,
The transcendent romance of the divine, joy!

When winter made its icy entry,
When the trees hastened to brace for change
And announced their goals in brilliant hues…
When laughter labored,
Assailed by fatigue…
When rest yielded,
Stressed upon itself…
When sinews of ignorant resistance snapped
And I twirled, abandoned in a whir of
Abundant knowledge,
And actively sought the ally of courage…
On one such day after my psyche had become
A cracking bed for thunder,
I turned to my God, saying:

'Arrayed before me is a breed of violent men,
They threaten to tug at my testicles.
My gall is already spilled in me,
And I am intoxicated by my own adrenaline.
And yet your voice urges me,
'Be not afraid.'

'All my trust is in you -
This you know, but
What should I say to my ulcerating stomach?
That I am not the man that I am?
Woe to this whimpering warrior
Who met death and fled
And has for him joined the ranks of levanters.

'Grant that in this forest of despair,
I shall be thrust upon that path of love,
God's face, wherefrom flows all good,
And from one good flows another.
That I, being am, a source of good,
Conceived in love by you, may ultimately
Through you become godsame.
Then would I await death with passion

Even as an adulterer
Awaits another stolen embrace.

'For my death would not my end be
Nor did my birth mark my beginning.
I happened as a thought happens
Being am a particle of your thought
Latent, imbued in you and forever and always,
A piece of you.

'Now, let me hear the glad news
Of your deliverance.
For you have usurped the life which you gave to me,
And my dues are now paid.
Disperse my hardship even
As the wind disperses shredded paper.
May a tender sprout of hope and glee
Emerge from my seed of despair.
Whereas the days when your heavy hands
Rested on my shoulders were long,
Let their uplifting not be short lived,
So that the mouth that sang songs of despair
May now sing songs of joy.

'Joy ineffable, amazing delight,
The thrill of a soul in upward flight,
The fusion of man and God
One light to one light, journey's end,
The transcendent romance of the divine, joy!

'If today I should pledge my vows,
Let it be that haven cast an inward glance
I should account of me as naught,
Except as yours divinely chosen.
And when your spirit is finally withdrawn
I shall be as a pebble that fell off the precipice
Into a mighty ocean and I, defined in this time
And truth co-ordinates shall be no more.

'Every man is a stain
On the body clothe of history.
When washed away,
His place will be no more.

'Above all things this I ask,
That when I am gone, still,
Let it matter that I lived.
For of the flesh,
There is but life and death
And not much else in between.
And of the soul, immortal impermanence.
Therefore, let me not live in fear of death,
But of the death of life,
Let me be thoroughly weary.

'In vain have I told myself,
That if all men felt wealth,
If life were fair and just,
If all were pleasant that affects a man,
The progress of men would creep indeed.

'Then I proclaimed your wisdom
And noted that equity was not your virtue.
You would call me judge of a false meter …
But men judge not on else, but feel.

'Often do I trip on your outstretched feet,
The knowledge of your ways
Is a perilous uphill climb.
But do dialogue with me,
Let our minds meet, even unintelligibly so.

'From informational dross and overload,
Spare me, so that I may bear
The tote of my blackness with joy.
If I may, let me undertake to interpret
To the white man, the burden of blackness.

But far be it from me, that I should
Seek consolation for being I that I am.

'My blackness precedes me.
Wherever I go, whatever I do,
The fear of alienation
Becomes an unshakeable shadow.

'Can a man separate himself from his shadow
Without casting a deep darkness about him,
Thus obliterating his very presence?

'Thus have I become misfortune's child,
Ill, the wind that bathes my forehead.
Thus, has my history become
A baleful record of setbacks -
One foot on the slimy road
Another in the thorny bush
But my heart looks up to the sun
And my wistful eyes
Dream of pride's new day.

'Hence, I beseech you
Most inexhaustible source of all goodness
That I may die giving;
Giving my gifts of blackness to the world.
That I may die accepting;
Accepting people's gifts of *colorness*
Without fear or favor.
That I may die shouting;
May my voice not be smothered
By the raucous din of violent men.
That I may die defiant;
Confronting men who still drive slaves.
That I may die not conforming;
With my back turned against the ways
Of sorrow, sin and hate, and arrogance
Which kills men's consciences.

That I may die standing;
Dying as a world citizen,
Bestriding the thinning river of injustice,
Embracing the universe that gave birth to me,
Bequeathing to her,
The fruits of my labor of love.

'For a trifling,
Men labor all night.
For a little more,
They forsake their friends.
When gain is assured,
They lose their religion.
Thus men toiled before my time.
When I became aware of myself,
I toiled as well.
I joined the race of rats
In the great urban sewer of life.

'Today, I look back
And I have not seen
The dividends of my toil,
Except a need to toil some more.
Surely you made men of faulty design
And I resent the man that I am.
If I could advise you, I would
Urge you to recreate men
For if the snake were to become a necktie,
It would not rest around my neck.

'Was I not whittled to a fragile shell,
Staved, and I died.
The sinking into an unfamiliar
Moss of despair was complete.
All that thrashing about and frantic cries
For help would not avail.
I was not vulnerable anymore.
Nothing was there to be vulnerable …

My worst fears had emerged an incubus
And had eaten me up. I slept.

'You did not do me
A favor by giving me
An awareness of self.
You demanded and I gave you
The very best of me …
Would you, thereby, traumatize me so?
Someday, we will dialogue.
You will indeed be called upon
To justify, by means of rigorous logic,
The ways of your divine mischief
And all that slush of circumstances.

'Upon this miry bog
Where we have played the game of sinking,
From this very spot where I sank
You will pull up a renascent me,
B*rinated* and watery, as yet with
Floundering steps, will run again.

'Thus did I traverse
The transcendental tunnel
Of death consciousness,
And with my death,
A lingering ripple of self-doubt.
Thus has my toil been long and hard
And by your grace,
Would I toil some more,
And some more, and some more
Until I attain my definition of greatness:
A man, universal, mentally athletic
Compassionate, driven by love incontinent
Relishing all that is just and fair.

'Grant, O Lord, my God,
That at the moment of my death

When that book of life is opened to me
When my life's passions, with youth,
Come streaming back to me …
That serene glow, the acknowledging,
The grasping, great graffiti
Of beatific hue, the deeds of my life,
Salty life, indeed great art form
Except when painted on the President's mansion.

'Whereas I lament a failed campaign,
I will campaign again.

'When I called, I heard not your voice
Then I called and called,
And when my strength was far spent,
I called on my last breath,
And I heard you say, 'Here I am.'

'Stricken and lonely,
Abandoned by men's community,
I felt a pat on my back,
I looked up and it was you,
Hand held out.
In my confusion, I wept.
I had always known that your friendship
Was my only possession. But,
Why do you come when my strength
Is far spent, as at today
When I am reeling from the affliction of my mind?

'I said when my spirit was stirred,
'Give me strength of arms to move
The universe in the direction of justice.'
I looked when my spirit was calm
And despaired in the atony of my forearms.

'Then I searched for me.
I searched for me

In the high places of wisdom,
And in the low places of foolishness.
In my sleep, my spirit wandered,
Looking for me.
When I awoke, I was with me
But I did not know me.

'I said to myself,
'Surely I am dissociating,
For there is me, and there is me
That does not know me, and hence
I shall balk, until I divine
The fate of this duality.'

Chapter 4

Voices

Have you seen that they killed Ofeke;
The strangers, they listened not to him.
Human life held no sanctity for them.
Ofeke was one of us, among us, a prophet,
Given to volubility and extraordinary
Language skills and we understood
He need not be understood.
His mission was to deliver, not intelligibly so.
The white men; they slew Ofeke,
Our beloved prattler, treasure's house.

While still praying, I was lifted in spirit,
Aloft a mighty body of water,
And I heard the voice of a woman, saying:

'The wild fire has caught the thatched hut.
Run, the floodgates are open
Of mysteries bold and deep…
The trudger at freedom's road is fainting,
Breathless, he has chanced
Upon his last strength,
Yet his destination lies afar off…
Behold, gauntly columns of humanity,
Feeble thermodynamic entities…
Behold the chains of class struggle
And domination leashed around their necks.'

Then we drifted inland,
Coursing our way along the banks of
A mighty river, that could have been the Mississippi,
Or perhaps the Savannah river,
Stopping momentarily,
I heard a melancholic tone
Sung in the manner of Negro spirituals, saying:

'Sons of our mother,
A dog gets lost who ignores his master's whistle.
A hunter goes empty handed who ignores
The tail of a quarry to seize upon its head.

'Brothers of the dark skin,
Do not forget the bush that
Fed you in times of hunger.
He who throws away his pumpkin seeds
Throws away his vegetables.
A farmer does not eat his seedlings.
Please come back home.
The night has come,
The red jungle rooster must roost.

What we sought in the forest was at home.
Those who are rejected,
Do not reject themselves.
Please come back home
For mine is greater than ours.'

Then I heard another voice saying,
'Tell them, tell them tried and true
Valiant revolutionaries,
Tell them that we are still ashamed of them.
Tell them that a child who is not moved
By his mother's tears is an evil child.
Tell them that a child who denies his parents
Calls himself a bastard.
Tell them that a child who insists that his mother
Not sleep, does not and will not sleep.
Tell them that the ewe that gave birth to a ram,
Gave birth to a hoodlum.'

Then the spirit directed me to
A clearing in a rain forest,
There, under an oil bean tree
Amidst the murmur of a handful,
A voice rang out saying,

'Strange lives we lead.
Mgbankwocha, *oraliser,*[1]
Voice of the weather-beaten gong,
Make songs about us, strange breed
Who all our lives fled mediocrity
But mediocrity enveloped us.

'Mgbankwocha, *oraliser,*
Serenader of the yam festival,
Can a pusillanimous man
Progressively emasculated
Avoid the throes of mediocrity?

'Mgbankwocha, *oraliser,*
The air trembles at your voice
And so it may, but sing
About he who trembles before another
About shame to the whimpering warriors
Who indulge in self-evisceration
And have abandoned the ways
Of the braves.'

Then the spirit took me back in time
To a slave ship, making its way across
The Atlantic. At the stern sat a woman.
She was Ofeke's brother, she cried,

'Ofeke was not mad, my brother,
He explained why he was not mad.
'They call me mad,' he says, 'because,
Before I am done delivering one line
Of thought, another enters my mind,
Requiring great exigency.' And then
He would add that his biggest problem
Was that he had too many appointments to honor.

'Have you seen that they killed Ofeke;
The strangers, they listened not to him.
Human life held no sanctity for them.
Ofeke was one of us, among us, a prophet,
Given to volubility and extraordinary
Language skills and we understood
He need not be understood.
His mission was to deliver, not intelligibly so.
The white men; they slew Ofeke,
Our beloved prattler, treasure's house.

'A mad man knows both his thoughts and intellect.
And so we advised them to let Ofeke be,
Yet, they slew Ofeke
And were first on his funeral day.

Where they had not buried them,
They looked for their treasures.
Where they had not hung them,
They looked for their clothes.
They went into the bush,
They cut down the sacred Iroko tree,
They rushed out to the trudging path
And asked the passersby
'Who cut down the sacred tree?'

'Asked to dip, he carried our soup pots.
We advised the white man that a head barred
From resting on its owner's hands may not also
Be barred from resting on its owner's neck.

'We asked the white man why he loved to kill,
He said, 'When a two tailed lizard is not killed
A three-tailed lizard soon appears.'
Then we asked what was wrong with
A three-tailed lizard, he said, 'Well, it
Has three tails.'

'Ofeke's only crime was that he reminded
The white man that black hens laid white eggs too.
And challenged him to cough any different than us.
Yet they slew Ofeke, who insisted that
A man wished well may not wish evil.

'When we complained we were thirsty,
They suggested we cut our throats.
We asked how one could cut his
Throat and live, they said,
'Solve one problem before the other.'
They took us for fools who would provide
Yams to accompany the snake's meat.

'We saw through their pranks, and yet
We would not desecrate the earth

With their blood. They called us
Brutes, savages, barbarians,
But it was us who loved freedom
And they were of the murderer's kin.'

Endnotes

[1] One who has the skill to convert ordinary prose to poetry.

Chapter 5

Willie Johnson

When the dignity of man is found at last,
All hands shall with one accord be joined,
And there shall gush forth from the wind,
Songs of praise to our God,
Mighty, powerful and fear worthy,
Who shall revive all withered plants,
And all desolate lands rejoice with verdure.
And the tumult of joyous ululation
Will be seen upon the face of the sea.

Then making our way back in time,
I found myself in Harlem,
Deserted, but for a wiry looking
Fellow, who walking up to me said:

'Sir, let Georgia be on your mind
For reasons other than the romance in a song.
For I have sought them,
And I have not found them
A memorial to black men lynched on her soil.

'Listen to the groans and sobs,
Listen as hatred played out itself,
Listen to the sound of death,
At the end of crying.
Listen to the hollering
As rigor mortis confirmed a sure death.

'Georgia, tell me not remorse, show remorse,
Not prescriptive legislation,
Show full reparation
In the sincere belief that
A wrong was done.

'Teacher, follow the echoes
Of their death knell,
When in Georgia, feel the earth
Red with their blood.
Make a hero's song, hoist a red flag
For them in your heart;
For the unknown black brothers
Whose groans of yesterday
Have become mine of today.

'Every race has its womenfolk.
Our men bore the indignities to our women.
We were mere rearers of labor hands.
We shed viscid streaks of ourselves

That the white man's estate might prosper
And even those whom they bred
They adjudged not pure.

'Weep with us that weep
The mighty tree is sick
The woodpecker will peck away.

'Is a nation greater than its people?
Do not a people make a nation
That makes a people?
Would men not often see the house of woods
And not the insidious handiwork of termites
In its bowels?

'For thus America rejoices
In the advancement of its white folks
And ignores the plight of its minorities
That would determine her ultimate destiny.

'See as the child imprints behavioral
Traits from the adult, the drug addict,
The judge from Texas will kill the child.

'Weep with us that weep,
An innocent child will die again.

'Teacher, as they would we ran,
We ran faster than they could,
They said, 'a debasing activity,
Befitting their ilk.'

'As they would we ran,
We ran away from the spots of prejudice.
The harder we ran, the harder they came.
Then we asked, 'spurn you not the act of running?'
They said, 'not when our wealth might be diluted.'

'As they would we ran,
We turned not against them but us.
Yet after us they ran.
Still when we won the race,
They said it lacked in grace.
But when we slipped and fell,
And sank in the quagmire of poverty,
They vaunted above our heads
And mocked our unremitting toil.

'I say to the old white woman
'There is war where brawn is needed.'
She says, ' Well fight, I provide the brain for
The application of your strength.'

'Teacher, my name is Willie,
Willie Johnson, from
Big Stone Gap, Virginia.
I am M.I.A.B.N.F.[1]
My brother was Keith.
He died in the streets of Harlem.
Like a sewer rat, before my very eyes,
He was run over by a white man's car.
He was hungry …
The defense claimed
He ran into the car in dazed drunkenness.
The priest said lofty prayers about
How he would reside in heaven.
Like a withered reed was Keith
That the trodder crushes in his wake.
Like a grain of sand,
Utterly, insignificantly, anonymous
In a sea shore of poverty
That the beachcomber presses
Underneath his feet.

'He was a faceless black man
As indistinct as the darkness

That covered his future
To be derided and feared
But not to be loved.
Like a playing mantis,
They postured in fight towards us
Although we had not held violent intentions.

'Did not my forebears till the field
Attacking the earth with solemn rage
So that produce may come of it?
And did they not say, 'see a breed
Of violent men indeed?'

'Can the sharecropper
Forget the toils before the harvest?
The ombrophobic² chicken would
Sooner forget the adult that plucked
It's feathers in the rainy season.

'My mother was Theresa,
Theresa Johnson. She had a song
'I have got the light of freedom,'
She sang, 'I will let it shine.'

''Even in the deep forlorn
Behind the prison wall,
Even in the gloomy darkness of melancholy
I affirm the light of freedom,'
She sang, 'I will let it shine.'

'My mother had a song,
She reflected that though dark
The light about her,
The out ringing of freedom songs
Kept her soul alit.
'I have got the light of freedom,'
She sang, 'I will let it shine.'

'I recall the reluming light,
The passion that was loosened,
When my mother sang her freedom songs
Deep affirmation in the dignity of man.

'Looking up she had sung,
'When the dignity of man is found at last,
Then the rat race is finally run.
All aching feet shall be lifted off the ground,
And all wandering minds a refuge found.
All listening ears shall hear,
The sweet songs of true liberty,
And all seeing eyes shall see
Spring anew and everlasting.

''When the dignity of man is found at last,
All hands shall with one accord be joined,
And there shall gush forth from the wind,
Songs of praise to our God,
Mighty, powerful and fear worthy,
Who shall revive all withered plants,
And all desolate lands rejoice with verdure.
And the tumult of joyous ululation
Will be seen upon the face of the sea.

''Awake! Awake from your spiritual slumber,
Awake with flutes and drums,
Awake with instruments of soulful music,
Awake for the wondrousness of our God
Shall be revealed, who
With man on earth would dwell.

''Though dark the ambience about me,'
She sang, 'I have got the light of freedom,
I will let it shine.'

'My mother taught me how
The songs of freedom ensured

The continual rebirth of the Negro courage,
And sustained an ever growing revivalism.
How in her lowly spirits,
Her mother before her,
And before her mother;
And in her high spirits,
Sang even more to
Forestall its foreshortening.
Much to the confoundment of those
Who sought their lives
And regaled on callously gotten profit.

'Fain would my life's span be shortened
By a pernicious system,
Dripping with sweats of prejudice.
But even if the light in me were snuffed,
Even if a whole sea of prejudice be poured
Upon this smoldering ember of human dignity,
Even if my memory be accompanied by all
The sordid trappings of the ghetto,
Let our freedom songs be a legacy
To that glow in the dark
That sustained us in the cotton
Fields of the South
And would guide us beyond
The squalid habitations of the North.

'My mother had the light of freedom
Please teacher, let it shine.

'Though faint the will to struggle on,
Though salty this taste of false freedom
Can we who have this far come
Abandon the tools of our liberation?
The songs of freedom that rose
Like molecules of a potent gas,
And filled with spiritual hope
Any void of despair in its path,

And became the renewing force of
The indomitable spirit of the African slave.

'My mother had the light of freedom
Please sir, let it shine.

'See, the lover and the hater attain the same end.
Therefore, let me hate my beloved country,
For it matters not what intent I hold,
Let me cry that forbidden cry!
Hate begets hate begets hate.
Violence begets naught but itself.

'Hate I must proclaim sir,
Can love emerge out of hate?
Can the mouth that speaks ill today
Speak well tomorrow?

'But how could I?
I am Willie of the unfinished childhood.
The ways of hope, of achieving,
The path of love, that bank of tenderness
Was not held before me
In the urban squalor of my birth.

'Growing up in the wrong neighborhood
Not much was expected of me
'Help yourself lazy black boy!' they yelled,
'There is equal opportunity,
This is the land of opportunity.'
Tunes of lunatics were these,
War cries of hate groups,
Blistering the calloused epidermis of my pain.
For, for us players, my short stick to their long stick,
My field of thorns to their grassy lawn,
My sweltering heat, their meadow lake,
My undulating field, their level field …

'Teacher, do not your people say
That the adult who challenges
A child to a wrestling match
Abuses the child?

'Still the pride of a bird is its feather.
The beauty of a bird is its pride.
The pride of a bird is feather deep.
So does the pride of a black man
Rest in the shallow concessions
To which he is allowed.

'Ask them,
Black man of the inner city,
Where is your pride?'
Do not think we would not notice.'

Then in a sudden change of scenery
I saw Willie outfitted in military fatigue
Along with fifty-eight thousand soldiers
Blacks and whites, and four hundred scantily
Clad black men. His tone grew quite militant
As he says,

'A white woman was raped,
A white cop was shot,
A black man must die.

'A black woman was raped,
A black cop was shot,
A black man may die.

'For four hundred years they raped us
Yet no white man died.
Rape: a universal outrage against women,
Who condemned the indignity you
Suffered us to bear?

'Black man, endangered, homeless,
Mendicant, beggars of freedom
Who received judicious legislations
That are injudiciously enforced.

'I see no black man any more.
There was I, and probably you,
The two of us holding the thin
Battlefront of extinction.
I see white men in black skins
Undergoing a terrible crisis of identity.

'I know of three black men,
One is a prisoner of the mind,
The other, a prisoner of the state,
And the other, a prisoner of the mind and the state.
And all of them are dangerous,
Cultural mutants with fleshy nose
And big, powerful black buttocks.

'Do not let go.
Do not let us die.
For the union has said,
'Whereas no apologies are due to the house nigger…
Whereas no apologies are due to the farm nigger…
Whereas we are not constrained to offer any reparations…
Whereas the niggers' toil will not be memorialized…
Whereas the nigger will soon die.'

'Hark! The plea of this orphan,
Do not let us die.
My mother is dead,
So is my father, my uncle, and my relatives
The villagers are all dead.
It is mid morning and
I have not seen a single soul.

'Nothing can assuage my grief,
Not even your verses of goodly craft.
Do not your people say
That the chicken's footsteps
Will always distract the kite?[3]

'I am a sole survivor,
I have left Big Stone Gap,
I have been to Mississippi,
To Alabama, to Louisiana, to Georgia,
I have yet to announce a new day to
A single black soul.
Surely, this is cultural genocide
And today is the morning after.

'Misty! Misty morning!
Nightmare to the roving eyes,
Damper of zeal, restrainer of fortitude,
I welcomed you in the jungles of Vietnam
Where my tired eyes closed in death's sleep as
I heard the gentle voice of the black child crying,
'Do not let us die!'

'Verse maker, enshrine our oppression with
Your verses so that generations to come will not forget
The ills done to us who should not die.
Beloved one of God most high, do not let us die.'

Overcome by profound sadness, I replied,

'Willie, I myself am dying
To this life, whose purpose
Is not merely to love,
For truly, if there were no haters
There would be no lovers.
I shall make haste to depart,
From this, meeks' earth,
This worthless pile of starch, whose elixir

Is distilled into the paroxysms of
Orgasmic muscles.
Men of discipline repudiated it,
Nwoye sang about it and
Our women dissembled over it.

'Groans are the cries of the elderly.
Grandmother, beauty's ornament,
Now I know why the streak of tears the night before.
Songs of sorrow are not the old woman's vales.

'A male child does not see his
Grandmother's private parts.
It is an abomination.
But there is none left to bury you.

'And today, the dead must bury the dead.

'Ideato, the elegist is dead,
Who will now compose elegies for you?

'Egede, the leader of the funeral dancers is dead.
Will you now go to your grave
Without a funeral dancer?

'Otingbodongbo, the *abia* musician is dead,
What will happen to the corpses of our titled men?

'Cadavers everywhere, black cadavers
I refuse to acknowledge that the corpse
Behind me is my mother's.
Mama, please do not die.
Father is sprawled across from her.
Papa, please do not die.
For who will tell me folk stories
About the ant and the cock
About the wily tortoise and his exploits ...

'Dead goats, dead cattles,
Dead squirrels, dead fowls,
Chizoba's cat is dead.
Uche's hunting dog is dead, lying at his feet.
The last log of wood is still smoldering.
Ifeoma's soup pot is still on fire.
Inside, a dead lizard that fell from the rafters.
Egodi, the newlywed is dead,
Twined arm in arm with her spouse -
Stinking, rumbling, army of maggots,
Clamorous horde of flies,
Rapacious, in reproductive frenzy, are
Plundering my dead brother's half-open eyes.'

Then Willie said,
'From where they were thrown
Overboard in the Atlantic,
I hear the voices of black men pleading,
'Do not let us die, black man to come.'
From the Savannah river, I hear their voices
Rising like angry bubbles from the riverbed
Saying, 'black man to come, do not let us die.'
From the cotton fields of Alabama,
I hear the broken voices of black virgins
Saying, 'black man to come, do not let us die.'

Willie had weighted me down with utter sadness
I interjected, reluctant to assume Willie's mandate,

'Why should I not let you die
For I an no more a verse maker than a verse maker
A mere teller of tales, and not even a happy one?'

Willie ignored me and continued,
'Beloved one, tell them in their ears,
Tell them, the tribunal in heaven,
Tell them, Ani,[4] god of your ancestors,

All truthfully, tell him who left you
To the vagaries of Izaka,
There, tell your tale of sorrow
About perfidies, about innocent blood,
And how the earth was desecrated with our blood.'

Then turning to the assembly behind him
Willie strained, like a soldier that he was,

'Cry holocaust, let tyrants tremble!
Awake and awake the dawn
Of new and just history
Let its reels roll.
For the wind of hate stalls,
Round and round it goes,
Nurtured by the ideals of treacherous men
And stoked by institutions,
Where men of learned unrighteousness
Are gathered to breed unrighteous laws
Far removed from the exigencies
Of fairness and substantial compassion.

'All soldiers of justice arise.
Black, white, yellow and red, arise.
Arise, for our cause is just.
Arise, pick arms and charge into the wind of hate.
Let new lines of war be drawn, the civil war anew,
Let Armageddon be, Gettysburg in our hearts.

'In thunder's voice,
The raging guns of battle,
The roaring cannons
Vomiting their contents in anger,
The rattling muskets,
Great grumbling machineries;
Let them eat up men
Still intent upon slavery
Gettysburg in our hearts.

'Fight on! Fight on!
Until hatred is driven to the outskirts,
Away from the Union.
And true emancipation is won
For Americans and for mankind
Gettysburg in our hearts.

'Stomp away we will,
With righteous indignation,
Upon all the fortresses of injustice
Until from Alaska to Australia,
And from Chile to Siberia,
All sons of men raise their hands
In triumph, proclaiming in unison,
Proclaiming slogans anew, 'dignity
At last, dignity.'

So saying Willie vanished
And all his assembly with him
I awoke, overwhelmed and distraught.
Coming to, I heard a faint drumbeat.
I banished it, being too distressed to listen
For Willie's mandate burdened my mind
For Willie had led an ordinary life it seems
And at death has become a warrior
Intent solely on death destroying.
As he gave us his ghost on that misty morning
In the jungles of Vietnam, it seems,
He reflected about Keith his brother,
And about Theresa his mother
And the harsh circumstances of their lives
And determined that they should not die.

Endnotes

[1] Missing in action, body not found.

[2] Afraid of rain.

[3] A kite is a species of hawk native to Eastern Nigeria.

[4] god of the Earth.

Chapter  6

Song Of The Fountain

O fountain of spring eternal,
I have drunk of you, no longer shall I thirst,
And you satisfy my hungry soul
With gifts, finest of wheat
And forever your flame of life renew.

It *was not so much Willie's song*
As it was the lucidity with which
He was perceived. I had absorbed
Every frame of his revelations
Much to my monomaniacal
Disposition on his songs.
About a couple of weeks later, I turned, penitent,
Knelt before my God saying:

'Silences, dazed silences,
When the thrusting is done,
Breath hurries to regain its cadence
And the moonlight tumbles in again,
Underscoring the power of amorous love.
Thus have many a woman breathed
Irregularly beside me.
Yet not even in a woman's
Lusty embrace have I found peace.

'I have seen and heard,
The vibrant music of the bongo,
The grace of the conga dance,
The melody of the boogie-woogie,
The unorchestrated songs of birds,
The expression of beauty and love
In the music of many nations,
And still has rest eluded me.

'Then I said, 'the ways of the Lord are
Pleasant and righteous altogether.
In the Lord's own house shall I dwell.
In the shadows of his wings will I rest content.'
For he has said, 'come, all that are
Heavily laden and I will give you rest.'
But today, I have become the worm
And you, the mighty elephant whose legs
Rest recklessly on my spine.

'Your ways have imperiled me so
That I have sometimes sought
The rest that accompanies the dead,
Until I perceived that only a fool
Presumes rest upon death.
For rest is the cessation of all consciousness.
Thus, I am a worthless agent of
Your worthily fancy, having no
Purpose to my existence except as a link
In your divine consciousness.
Therefore, let not men presume
Their activities have a bearing
On your wellness, for so in hankering
After heavenly paradise, men have knelt
In fervent outpouring, restraining from what
Evil they may, that the Lord might rejoice.

'Your laws, O lord, are fundamental,
Perfect, they revive solely the souls
Of men, not yours. In keeping them
There is great reward; freedom from
Mundanities and partial rest.
Therefore, as I must live not for you,
But for me, let me abide by your
Will and hold not unto any capriciousness.

'Even as the wildebeest awaits the first monsoon,
Even as a watchman awaits the dawn,
Even as a child awaits its mother,
So do I await the return of your grace,
That I may be guided towards that light
Of matchless brilliance.

'Like the matutinal soil,
Sated of the morning dew,
Let your kindness be manifest upon me
For in you is my salvation.

'For of all who show mercy,
You are the best.
Of all who love,
Who is tenderer than you?
Of all who inspire
Who is greater?
Of all who console,
Who is more compassionate?

'In you is my salvation,
Mercy, dear Lord, mercy,
For you are truly best at showing mercy.

'Wisdom is your greatest act of mercy
And you give it to whom you will.
Of those whom you have given wisdom,
They have been blessed abundantly.
But none remembers except whom you
Inspire to remember.

'Before you then I come,
A connoisseur by appellation;
An undiscerning wine taster that I am
Of unremitting thirst, and I taste.
As often as I have, I yield
That you, O lord, are good.

'O fountain of spring eternal,
I have drunk of you, no longer shall I thirst,
And you satisfy my hungry soul
With gifts finest of wheat
And forever your flame of life renew.

'I have seen the thrust of another autumn,
The thunderclap of another summer,
The days of more lives and
Those who would live forever
Have taken a stand against he that cries

From the wild and tell fabled
Tales of mice and men.

'Lord, you are he that desires
Truth in your inward being.
Being that I also desire truth,
Then I am god-same.
But being that I, not you, are
Transformed by truth, then you are
Truth itself. Since I desire truth
I must desire you - you being
The truth, the way and the life.
Hence, I say, 'come, O my God
Come, come, you will be loved.'

'Lord, spare me the mentality
Of pearly gates and forever paradise,
For there is nothing else to be desired
But truth - the ultimate reward of which
Is freedom. You the truth make men free
And there is no state greater than freedom.

'O lord, you are the truth,
And the truth is expressed in words
And the word is you.
Since the truth cannot be known
Without the word, the word is the truth
And your inner being is the spirit of the word.

'Your sentience, O lord, is felt
In the interstices of my innermost thoughts.
Would that they go forth without
Your divine approbation,
Would they not be short lived?
Thus, it is altogether fitting,
That I yield all of them to you.
So that you, carrying out
My chores of thinking,

And I being am, a mere channeler,
May become a bud in the great tree
That is your godhead.

'Then would you restore laughter to my face,
Giving me back a world of idling
And innocence, and joy
As boundless as the blue sky.
For to all men, all things may I be,
But to you, may you say,
'He delights in my will
And his ways make me proud.'

'These things I hold to be
Incontrovertibly true,
That every day had its dawn,
Every adult, a childhood,
Every final moment, an inception;
That nothing had an ending
That did not have a beginning.

'Since you do not have an ending,
You do not have a beginning.
Since nothing exists that did not become,
Then you do not exist.
Yet since I yield that you exist,
I must yield a becomeness to you.
Since you have become,
Then, you too will die.
Logical cul de sac.

'Are you totally incomprehensible to me?
For it is either that you exist
Because I exist, thus making you my
Illogical creation, or that you became
When you became, not as an inception
But as a continuum- thus making
You an inexistable form.

'Therefore, I yield a becomeness to you
As much as I am inclined to yield
A nonbecomeness to you.
However, the manifestations of your infinite
Wisdom and the limited dimensionality
Of my thoughts, leave me no other choice
But to proclaim your existence,
Since to proclaim your nonexistence
Would negate my own existence.
Thus are we like garlands,
Linked arm in arm, creator to creature.

'Because I create it, a thought becomes.
I yield it and it exists.
A creation thus has an inception,
The beginning of its existence.
Since I yield that you exist,
I should yield a creator to you.
Since there is no creator besides you,
I yield that you are capable of self-creation.

'Although the logical loop is now tied,
You are still incomprehensible to me
Creator of the creator,
Beginning of the beginning
Simultaneously transcendent and immanent.

'Since I cannot understand your beginning
How could I understand your ending?
Thus, to linearize your existence
Would be logical futility.
Could it then be that you are
At once ending and beginning?
You must be the beginning and the end
Simultaneously, just like eternity
Is the ending and the beginning
In the same continuous time frame.

'Then, O lord, my God, I proclaim
All men, the God I see and you
The God I do not see.
Are you thereby fully defined for me
In body and in spirit.
Even as I must love you,
So must I love all men.

'No one knows you my Lord,
But all are known by you.
He that declares he is pursued
By the land, let him also declare
On what footage he intends
To outrun the land.
When I declare that I am
Oppressed by you, let me also
Declare on whom I rely for help.

'Remember John, my brother, the mad trotter,
Who never walks and was asked
Why he was constantly running.
He said he was being pursued by the land,
But could not outrun the land.
Such are you, my Lord.
Since I cannot even momentarily
Detach myself from you, so as
To subject you to objective analysis,
I must then assume that you and I are one.

'You are contained in me
And I am contained in you.
However, you are in all of matter
And I am in me, but through you
In all of matter. By being in you,
The intricate web of life, the labyrinth
That links the inanimate to the animate
The spiritual to the contraspiritual
And the temporal have all become closed.

I then proclaim myself
A godsame, a god minor,
But only by you, a purposeful being.

'O lord, my God, you are it.
As nothing is, so are you.
You are the *unitive-cognate*[1] integral of existence.
You are both the agency and the agent,
The awareness and the *awareform*,[2]
He that permeates and are permeated,
He that determines and are determined,
All of matter is you and you are all of matter.
That I am alive is simply the affirmation
Of your existence, not mine.
That I am not alive does not negate
Your existence, but mine.

'O lord, my God, you are not amenable
To linear logic. You are it that sheds
And are shed, but are not depleted.
You are nothing, but that nothing
That anchors and I am that anchorage
Dependent particle of you ...
Your creature, no less you, than yourself.

'O lord, my God, the intransmutable
Transmuter, the immutable mutator,
You perplex me! You drive me to desperation.
You bewilder me. By our interdependence,
I am thoroughly confused.

'That I am, this now I know, possibly dead,
Uterined in your consciousness,
Submitted to usury and anguish,
Awaiting rebirth, via that lighted tunnel
Wedged between your cellulite-laden legs.

'Still with these rudiments say I,
Wonderful are your ways,
In wisdom you conduct your affairs.

'O plenary days of immortality,
As yet undiminished and undiminishable,
O that the immensity of the universe
Would at time's end, collapse to
Your glorious nothingness, and I,
Not existing in time, would at time's end
Exist as part of your majestic godhead.
This, O Lord, being my destiny,
I beg of you to grant, at this
Fleeting moment of my nonexistence,
A knowledge of your truth
And the full ecstasy of your awakening.

'Rise with me, O moon,
To the heavens let my heart be lifted.
There in hope and pride and blood,
There with men whom fear have overcome,
Whose sweat, agony and tears moisten my vocal chords,
My voice, immortal, extols my God.

'Speak thou to me.
Let not the blessed Mohammed,
Let not Moses nor Elijah,
Let not any who inspires not speak to me.
Speak thou to me, O God of my life,
And Lord of all creation.
Even as the breath of an amorous
Lover quickens besides her love,
Let me feel the breath of your love today,
So that I may reach out and touch your face divine.'

Endnotes

[1] The singular kinship shared by all creation – seen and unseen.

[2] The power to enlighten and that which is the subject of the enlightenment.

Chapter 7

Footsteps
On The Anthill

Have you seen that a dog has eaten a fellow dog!

Children of my father, please behold with me,

The August wind, the abandoned nest, the dead birds,

The cries of a bird, the sore on its mouth, the dying bird,

The troubled tree, the monkeys who treasure it,

The grazing sheep, the contemplative python,

The thirsty antelope, the crocodile infested water,

The caged rat, the company of a snake,

The fish, the pond full of alligators,

The snail... before which lies a thorny landscape,

The wooden gong, fustily hailing the dead man.

While *thus agitated in spirit,*
I *was alerted at the sound*
Of *a strident and powerful voice,*
Pitchy *as of a woman's voice,*
Like *a thousand crickets crying*
Synchronously, *piercing the maze*
That *was my thoughts.*

She began,
'Can the tiger lose its stripes,
The leopard its spot,
The elephant its *elaphantitude,*
The brooding hen her *chuckability.*

'Must the Ethiopian be bothered
By the color of his skin?
Do they not also kings and wisemen make?'

'No,' I protested, 'No, No.
Why should the mighty beast not growl?
And the predator not lie in stealth?
For it is their nature, this I know
But the race is not to the swift,
Nor the advantage in war to the berserk,
Nor is victory the preserve of the growler.

'Does the warrior not die
In all his intensity?
Does his viciousness
Not fail to avail him?
Might it then not behoove
The tiger to shed its *tigritude,*
And the elephant, its *elephantitude?*
Before the hovering hawk,
A prudent hen chucks not.'

At *this point, I heard the faint beating of*
A *drum that seemed to be saying,*

'Every *rodent, find a hole, find a hole.'*

Ignoring *me, the voice went on,*

'The prowler cannot find the prey.
The gods cannot be appeased.
The venomous snake has been spotted
In the nook, and there is another on the
Thatched roof, and another has slipped
In through the cracks.

'We have heard the ominous cries
Of *agunkwo*, the mourning bird,
Announcer of death's day.
Confusion and despair is loosed upon our world.

'Flee, without mate or company, flee!
Without kids or wives, flee!
Without grimace, shout or strain, flee!
The ubiquitous cloud of destruction, flee!
The rumbling earth will reckon
With its desecrators,
For none can avail the other
Nor can any be helped, flee!
The helpless infants must avail themselves,
The old woman, the devices of her limbs;
Flee, for death's day is upon us
And intellectual calisthenics will no longer
Substitute for true illumination.'

Confused, *I said somewhat angrily,*

'Should I ask a strange woman to close
Her mouth, do I know if she eats flies?'
At which she retorted sharply,

'Dilettantism, you are the treacherous
Lamp bearer that blew out the guiding light
In the middle of the stony road.'

Then in a mellow voice, she continued,

'Have adversities driven you offshore?
Have you become one of those
Whose achievements will be measured,
Not by the successes you attained
But by the adversities you overcame?
Have you thus become a rudderless ship,
Resigned to fate's twists and turns?

'Are you tethered?
Are you determined by another?
Have you lost a race that
Has not yet begun?

'Have you drunk water?
Has it lingered on your teeth?

'Have you been to gather firewood in the dry season,
Did the skies suddenly let go of their rein on rain?

'Did you provide the sweat and blood,
And were you not invited to the victory feast?

'Are you like the morning star
Who guided an ungrateful night
To the beginning of a new day,
Whereupon reaching its destination
It reminded you that a star
May only be seen at night?

'Were you ignored
When reparations were offered
To those who were far less dispossessed than you?

'Did you till the ground
And plant the white yam
And were you given *abana*[1]
On the day of the bumper harvest?

'About freedom, were you told,
Wait, until such a time, wait
And was it not granted to those
Who came before and after you?

'Have you put in more and gotten less?
Has your cup refused to flow over
Even though you poured in more
Than your neighbor whose cup now overflows?

'Have you slain the lion?
Was it charged that you killed a weak and sleeping lion,
And your heroics thereby discounted?

'Have you gathered more firewood
Than your fellows, and was it declared
That you gathered yours from the
Evil and forbidden forest?

'Are you like the lone traveler
Whom fate, without a hint,
Constantly brings to the road
Of seven splinters?'

Then in a sudden change of pace, she cried,

'*Tile le tile le Koti lele,*
When adults conspire in child abuse,
There can be no rejoicing.
Koti lele.'

Continuing on in a rapid and intense tone, she said,

'Did the tortoise suddenly become a proficient climber
On the day you finally elected to go hunting?

'Have you seen that children are hunting for roasted rats
In the midst of burning huts?
On this, our land, that fed the grapefruit
That would not feed the land.
With these, our hands that washed
That would not be washed.

'Have you seen that those with whom
We hunted lizards are now hunting for rats?
And behind our backs, they announce in jest,
'He who marries his friend's child marries too late.'

'Has your master given you a bag of salt for your wages
And sought the rainmaker soon afterwards?

'Have you cut your palm fruit,
Has it fallen irretrievably into a marshy ground?

'Hunger kills that has no hope…
Have you been allotted a barren land
Upon which to sow?

'Would our corpses be accompanied
By goat meat over which
There has been much squabbling?

'Listen, listen to Nwaokoye of Uruagu Otenyi
Who wishes still birth upon pregnant women
Since his wife's womb was dry.
Nwaokoye, would you burn a bridge and forget
Your homeward journey?'

Mellowing off again, she continued,

'The rebel is docile,
The podium is dismounted
But the reform has not yet begun.

'See, the gathering of a million *thesisists*
The paralyzing shot of a thousand critics
And men who dared to direct our thoughts.'

Now accompanied by a more vibrant rhythm
From the ever present drummer
Amidst the stirring as of a small crowd,
She continued, matching her delivery
To the cadence of the drum,

'Children of Owelle, gather around and share my vision.
Have you seen that a dog has eaten a fellow dog?
Children of my father, please behold with me,
The August wind, the abandoned nest, the dead birds,
The cries of a bird, the sore on its mouth, the dying bird,
The troubled tree, the monkeys who treasure it,
The grazing sheep, the contemplative python,
The thirsty antelope, the crocodile infested water,
The caged rat, the company of a snake,
The fish, the pond full of alligators,
The snail… before which lies a thorny landscape,
The wooden gong, fustily hailing the dead man.

'Anyaegbuna, the reptile's eggs
Have refused to hatch.
They demand a sitter.
Can the cold-blooded reptile sit upon its eggs?
See how the laws of nature
Have fallen hostage to the whims of men.

'The cockroach assumes it is a hawk,
It should be left alone,
Until it visits the homestead of the chicken…

'The rooster rejoices,
He says he invented sunrise…
But on the feast of yams,
Sunrise slipped by the mighty cockerel.

'Nwachi, has the nesting bird been shot?
What may now become of her young ones?

'Ngozi, the burrows have collapsed
Under the furious hack of hoes…
What may become of the young rodents?

'The burrowing ant assumes its powerful
Thighs trigger earthquakes.
It is best left to its world.
Behold another unwitting footstep
On the anthill… Cataclysm…
The ants hold their vigil…

'Nkemjika, the stranger has trampled
Our newly hatched chicken.[2]
How must we now receive him?

'Nnamdi, the arrow of god has caught its target.
When the mighty tree falls, the birds disperse.
On whose cause shall we now rally?

'Tobe, have you seen that the mountain goat
Is weary of rocks and slopes,
And his randy land-dwelling counterpart
Is weary of mating?

'Have you seen that what is greater than the termite
Has entered the termite's tiny hole?

'Have you seen that the tortoise's rhythm
Is *malubido, malubido,* but the troublemaker
Insists it is *ralakata, ralakata?*

'Have you seen that the antelope
Has abandoned *tum tum gem gem*
And runs to a different rhythm?

'Have you seen that the swine
Has lost its taste for acorns,
And the manatee is sick of seaweeds,
And the barking dogs have forgone
Their chief delight,
And the hounding dogs now despise
Swiftness of feet,
And their blood is no longer
Stirred by an earnest tallyho?

'Chibu, have you seen that the hunter
Has become squeamish over carcasses, and
Forlorn, he has tossed his gun aside?

''*Oh Oh Ya Oh OOh!*'
Says the impotent groom,
'What a miserable existence.'
'What use is a fat breast
That would not suckle a male child?'
Says the impatient farmer of his barren wife.
'When will my dying days come?'
Says Itulu, the quadriplegic.

'And there was profound despair.
A thick cloud of misery hung overcast.

'Onyinye, the wind and the wild fire
Are ravaging our huts.
Askant; the leisure walkers ought
To be pressed with a thousand cares,
Care-worn, they have not even quickened their steps.

'Uvoko, the idols upended
By the combating bantams

Are yet to be righted
And they stare at us in their full portent.

'Uduni, the old woman's dog
Has bitten through the bony pendant
On her neck. She would not let go
Although she could not provide for it.
Would the dog not eat her corpse?

'Udensi, has the nursing goat
Abandoned juicy fodder to infant's feces?
''Of the pot bellied men,'
The dog once said, 'let every dog
A companion make, for if
He does not throw up, he will
Certainly make voluminous feces.'
And the other dog said, 'second
To the pot bellied man is
The medicine man. His kind
Is given to the most oily feces.'
Yet, we have not seen any dogs
Trailing the potbellied or the medicine man.

'People of Ezi Owelle,
Have the bright petals of spring
Donned the sullenness of drought?
Has the sun died at noonday?
Has the dark cloud of hate
Eclipsed our luminous friend?

'Udensi, recall on the eve of the gods,
That gray cloud of locust.
Today, the dark cloud of hate,
They eclipse our luminous friends.

'Has the rising sun not lost its reliability.
Upon setting, has it not taken a route
To which it is unaccustomed?

Would it get lost?
Would our sun rise again?
O! How anxiety has consumed us.

'Osita, the fish holds water in loathe,
The earth insists it is
No longer accustomed to corpses.
How might we dispose of our dead ones?

'Udenka, the contractions of child birth
Have visited the *osu*[3] girl and
There is no one willing to aid her!

'Mgba, it is customary to untether
A she-goat suffering the pangs of parturition.
Have you seen that the wailing goat
Is still tethered?
The adults are preoccupied,
An elder has just passed away.

'Omunu, the snake has slipped into
The burrow. Must the rodent,
Abandon its watery infants and flee?

'Omunu, the sitting bird has been shot,
Her eggs will come to term tomorrow.
Tomorrow, the wild lizard will laugh aloud.

'Have you seen that the sky is free
Of the reconnaissance of the bird of prey.
And the nesting eagle has abandoned
Her nest and fled, an intruder has been spotted.
Again, her best efforts have been thwarted.
Her distress has multiplied.
She must fly to the ends of the earth
To lay her eggs, free from intrusion.
But men now habit the ends of the earth,
And we have heard her weeping,

'Tilele tilele kotilele, kotilelo O!
Tilele tilele kotilele, kotilele!''

There was a long pause and I heard
The murmuring as of a group of people.
When they settled down a bit, she continued,

'Can the lion shed its pride
And still be called a lion?
Can the hen cease to chuck
And still keep her family together?
Can a black man not be black
And still call himself black?'

Drumbeat! Drumbeat!

Life is a travesty.
There is no man carried on the head
Who has a good pair of buttocks.
'Life is a travesty,' says the millipede,
'For he that was trampled is not crying
The trampler loses his soul in tears.'

Endnotes

[1] An unpleasant tasting yam species that preserves rather well.

[2] It is considered a bad omen to trample someone else's chicken.

[3] A pariah. A social class among the pre-colonial Igbos said to be
dedicated to deities. The concept of osu is now largely discredited.

Chapter 8

The First Encounter

The tide has carried the newly hatched

Tadpoles out to the turbulent stream,

They will make fodder for the fish.

The stream has overwhelmed the aged frog.

The old owl is finally overburdened by the size of its head.

How was I to know that a fire

Does not recognize who fetched it

And tenderly brought it to being?

Has it not left the pot to kill

The contents of the pot?

Has it not crossed the stream to kill a spawning toad?

And now only blinking awaits the eyes.

It had been four weeks since I heard
The lamentations of the woman
Whom I later learnt was the legendary
Poet and griot, Nwabuno.
My mood was inconsolable
And my disposition leery at best.
One evening, just after sunset,
I laid down to sleep, but was awoken
By the disconcerting sound of drums.
I knew the drummer was around and I braced for
What else might follow. As the drummer approached,
I felt the presence of three other fellows.
They spoke in turn, adopting a relaxed,
Conversational mode of poetry.
The first voice said,

'A man is not seen without his fleshy nose
Or a bullock, its strong hooves.
The night may be stronger than the brave,
But a warrior is known by his footsteps.
A newborn is named according to his countenance
And this one shall I name,
The beautiful sun-draped stone of Uzoakoli

'Every child is as precious as an only palm kernel
We will not let him get lost in the fire.
'Ebenebe,' he continued,
'He who stares at a stronger man
Merely admires him.
Still let the hand that planted the dry season
Reap its fruits.
If life were a thread,
Would our enemies not certainly cut it?
But the earth does not swallow a sacrifice
For the palm frond always falls inbounds.

'When the great palm tree falls,
Women clamber all over it.

When fire smolders, it is as if it is dead.
Nwoye, hardly is the fall of the bread fruit
Not accompanied by ingrained sand.'

Then the second voice said,
'Ezenwanmadu, a squirrel does not sire a skunk.
It is true that the dividend due a hero is mere praise,
But a dancing goat praised, breaks its legs.
The footwork of the antelope
Is best displayed on a rugged hillside.
Therefore, let the boastful wrestler,
Wrestle the ground.

'Let thunder trim the big dead limb of a tree
That rejoices at the sight of a child.
Let he who is fascinated by a dog's nose
Be served the nose of a dead dog.
Let he who awakens the child of *okwa*,[1] not sleep.
He who murders a child,
What could a child have possibly done to him?
Should the goat-killing lion boast of his strength?
Should not the jaw eater first feel out his own jaw?

'Nwoye, do we not say that the chicken that rejoices
At the sight of the scorpion should beware of its tail?'

Then the third voice spoke,
'True, what bit a dog to death really bites
But a stranger is not praised
Before his deeds are seen.
Often times, a child assumes that the sole purpose of life
Is to be well fed.
The incontinent child who ruins his mat
Should sleep on the floor.
The monkey who ate the cob of corn
Should not be served a drink of water.
'Ezenwanmadu, if he who destroys an idol does not fall,
Hardly does he appreciate the help of the medicine man.

'Why should the mighty tree assume
That its waist is the greatest thing that rots in the bush?
Still, I agree that a goat's teeth are not trimmed
On the day it ate yams.
'Okonkwo,[2] let he who insists
That a head is needed for sacrifice
First consider his own head.'

Then I said,
'O fellows, why may I not sleep
When there are no coal embers on my thatched roof?
Still, murk is the reply to a speech unseen,
For where lies a speech, lies its reply.
I am advised that silence is a potent speech.
The woman who sees me and remembers
How her child was knocked to death by a withered tree,
Let the fate of her child befall her.'

Then the first voice spoke,
'The dog said that those who have buttocks
Do not know how to sit.
We were expecting the withered tree to fall,
The live one fell.
When an egg cracks nuts,
The stones should cover their faces in shame.
But Nwoye, a corpse is borne by its owners,
No matter how it died.'

'Yes Ezenwanmadu, but there is no art
To tell a man who bathes fully clothed.
The child who would not fight probably
Started the fight in the playground.
Ebenebe, when we look for the eyes of a carcass,
Do we not go to the head?'

Then Ebenebe replied,
'Nwoye, is that not why on the inquest of the missing fruit,
The monkey would not testify for the offspring on her back

Because she would not know if it reached up
And plucked the fruit?
Still, a battleground is not without blood.
Should we not seek out the widow's knife
If we must know what she had for dinner?'

Then Ezenwanmadu said,
'Ah, the kitchen knives in a widow's house,
The sharp ones have no handle,
The behandled ones are never sharp.
I say, the gunpowder is sooner exhausted
If we must track a lizard's trail up a tree.'

Okonkwo came to my defense, saying,
'The man who insists that a knife is not sharp,
Let him scrape off the dust on his cornea with it.
He who was not there when a corpse was buried
Always exhumes from the legs.'

Ezenwanmadu said,
'Cowards spoil for a fight
When a weakling is seen.
Like the tortoise whose alleged strength
Is freely displayed in the field of mushrooms.
Ebenebe, the absence of vultures on the day of sacrifice
Is an indication of displeasure in the land of spirits.'

Then Ebenebe said,
'We fault elders for not talking;
For not listening, we fault kids.
Still, not with the same instrument
Do we cleanse the eyes and the ears.
The man whose father was killed by the buffalo,
Does not drink off the buffalo's horn.
But the traveler who winds up in the land of ear cutters
Ends up with a cut ear.
Nwoye, it is my observation that
The dog eats feces,

But it is the goat whose teeth are rotten.'

Then Nwoye spoke,
'I feel like the mother of a bad child
Who must excuse her son before a gathering of elders.
Could he be the knife that was urged to be a knife
That demanded to be the kitchen knife?[3]
Has no one noticed that the chicken that farts
Is pursued by the land?[4]
Even then, all lizards are reptant,
How could you tell which has stomach ailment?
The rat who sports with the lizard on a
Rainy day is foolhardy.

'Let he who dreams big be presented
With the jaws of the male elephant.
Indeed, how often men spoil for war when we
Romanticize the tales of war heroes.
But war is a deadly game
That even angels fear to play.'

Resenting Nwoye's speech, I replied angrily,
'The droppings made by a flying bird
Lead one to imagine how much more
It intends to make upon perching.
It is true that not owning up to how much they eat
Is why women have no beard
But the person who tells all his problems, loses respect.'

'Like the foolish man who sought shelter
After he was already drenched…
Son, he whose palm kernels is one left
Has none left,' Nwoye said.

After an uncomfortable silence, Nwoye continued,
'We do not see with other people's eyes.
A lizard that does not behave like one
Will be roasted for sure.

Besides, the stick which is likened to a snake
Is often much bigger than the snake.
The person who steals fresh fish
Gets caught with its bones in his throat.
It has always been my experience that
A long legged goat jumps the fence.
The child who bears both knife and fire
Usually gets imperiled by one of them.'

Sensing Nwoye's belligerency, Ezenwanmadu said,
'Nwoye, a bird thrown upwards
Is shown the way to his mother's land.
Mischief thrills when you are not the victim.
Nwoye, leave head butting for those who have heads.
A single hand does not tie a parcel.
A pregnant bat is not known from the ground.
He who has never sustained an injury
To his throat does not appreciate that every feast
Is accompanied by saliva.'

Ebenebe also addressed Nwoye, saying:
'Nwoye, a child does not defecate in a bush
Where the grass is taller than he is.
He who eats locust from the bottom of the dish
Does not realize when they are finished.
Be not like the old woman who prays for diarrhea
Upon reaching a clearing in the forest,
Or like Ofeke, who takes two goatskin bags
When there are not enough to go around.
Let the trigger-happy man shoot his plantains;
Guns his, plantains his.
We are complaining of an epidemic of filariasis,
You are wishing flatulent stomach
Upon a man with elephantiasis of the scrotum.
Nwoye, do not let this jointly owned goat
Sleep in the fields.
After all, it is with the feet that we seek valuables
That fall into the river.'

Then Nwoye replied,
'The chicken kills before it eats.
We go to the kings to carouse and revel.
When a kleptomaniac is being counseled,
He plans for more places to rob.
All I can say is that
Feces smell. Bad feces smell bad.'

Then I said to Nwoye,
'There is no easy route to Umuahia.[5]
Often, the quack medicine man requests for
The heart of an ant.
Even then, a dog is not in the habit of brushing its teeth.
Nwoye, the hen walks, the chicks trot
But I would not ask a goat to accompany
Me to the yam barn.
I am the spirit to your giant footsteps,
The rock to your spear,
I refuse to be impressed.
Words are like oceans to your mouth,
How could they possibly dry?
He who invites me to match proverbs,
Implores my tutelage.'

Turning aside, I plunged into a monologue
Making it clear that their intrusion was not welcomed.
'He who was bitten by a snake
Fears the head of a lizard.
The buttock bitten by a scorpion soon learns.
Knowing that death comes from above,
Has the chicken not adopted the habit of searching
The skies in between mouthfuls of water?
Moreover, the squatting toad said it has just sent for
Its mother's chair and need not be roused.

'The tortoise said it knew of its mother's impending death,
When it called the dog and it responded.
The man of many thoughts does not respond to idle talk.

Besides, the mortar that carries food
Turns its back to the ground.[6]

'How should I make it clear that a craftsman
In the middle of a task is unwelcoming,
Or that I am a land dweller
Who has no need to steal the sacrificial meat?
Was it not the chicken who said that by the time
It has gathered food for his personal god,
Then his gizzard, then himself, he perceives that
The day is short indeed?[7]

'O mystery fellows, the lying goat
Lies on its hide.' I concluded.

Again the fellows spoke in turn,
Starting with Ezenwammadu,
Who sounding quite avuncular, said,
'Would the dog not sooner decline food
Than ignore its owner's call?
Son, please ignore Nwoye.
He who seeks an altercation said
The chameleon broke his plates.
An impeccably beautiful woman that must be faulted
Is told that her legs are tiny and crooked.
The palm fruit that falls into the soup pot
Has certainly reached its home.
Nwoye, a stranger's corpse sometimes feels like a log,
But the woman with many children
Is accustomed to staying awake.'

Then Ebenebe said,
'Nwoye, a dog that is fond of raw meat
Runs after the man with elephantiasis.
We are talking about a woman that drowned,
You are talking about the cloth on her waist.
The fact that we sometimes fall for laughter
Does not mean that laughter is a wrestler.

The drainer of ponds,
Does he also drain the sea?
Was it not the crab who said that it has two heads
So that it may have two chances at life
But death struck him in the middle?

'When you see an Alzheimeric old woman
Eating the droppings of a chicken, stop her.
The infection she contacts usually goes around.
Nwoye, look at a child's face before you eat off his hands.'

Nwoye replied,
'Have you not seen that the broom that
Swept the frontage, swept the house?
Can pregnancy be covered with the palms of one's hands?
Ebenebe, a child on its mother's back
Does not realize that the road is far and arduous.
I would not spoil a child just because
He might be the reincarnation of my father.
I still say that a thief's disposition is seen on his face.'

Taking umbrage at Nwoye, I *turned towards him, saying,*
'By this the chicken knows that it has princely blood;
That men elect to carry it on their heads.
Nwoye, let the boxer box the head of a palm fruit.[8]
Let the mighty wrestler wrestle the ground.
It seems that the eye that eyes meat eyes nothing else.
A child who perceives fair treatment is happy.
After all, the palm kernel which a child desires
Will not ache him afterwards.

'Nwoye, let me be
For where a worm dies is its burial ground.
Just remind my kinsmen that the good done
To a dead person is an expeditious burial.'

'Let he who died a coward
Not expect a well-attended funeral,' Nwoye said.

I *replied,*
'The stomach could not be a coward
And still elect to bring the fore of the body.
Could you not count your teeth with your tongue?
Or is it hard to see that the tortoise resents
The fact that it has no long tail?
Yes, Nwoye, I am a crab eater,
There is no secret dining place for that relish.

'Was it not the fly who said that those with open sores
Do not travel unmolested through its father's estate?
 If you must insist that the frog grows beard
Just understand that it will not get married.
Nwoye, a man who tells all he heard, gossips.'

Okonkwo, who had been quiet all this while
Finally intervened,
'Nwoye, a man whose house is on fire
Does not search for roasted rats.
Is a monkey not best caught by stealth?
Only he who is familiar with a dog's disposition
Sticks his hand in its mouth.
Men of Ezira, this child is still a scorpion
That does not know its alleged parents.'[9]

Then Nwoye said,
'Okonkwo, a transgressor runs
When he is not being pursued.
The debtor's heart fibrillates
When the cock crows.
Can one yell thief
And insist on not being helped?'

Then I replied,
'No, a man's headache is often as big as his head,
But a big head is not known to overburden its bearer.
Where lies a corpse, lie its mourners and rejoicers.
Has it not occurred to you that the

Worm that died in the barn did not die of hunger?
Nwoye, let the corn tell how it should be eaten.'

In response, Nwoye said,
'Okonkwo, uneasy lies the mind that foments evil.
He who knows evil is known by it.
The eater of *abana*[10] exposes his teeth to his personal god.
The imprudent animal that fell into a ditch killed itself.
Much like the hapless man who fell into the frigid river
And claimed he had a sudden desire for a cold bath.'

Nwoye had baited me again and my patience
Was beginning to thin out quite a bit.
I said to him,
'The palm kernel eater does not know
When the cracking stone gets angry.
Was it not *Akpakoro* who said that
His hands have not left the spear
Since his last fight with the sky?

'Nwoye, have I not said that the hen
That drinks and looks up harbors of an ill done to her?
It is true that the ants own the palm top,
The antelopes, the grassy plain,
But still, the frog feels the heat of the ground.

'Nwoye, if your fervent inquiries earn you a dog's head
What might you do with its jaws?
How do you come off like the home-ridden cripple
Who assumes he knows everything that happened
In the market place?

'Nwoye, if you must know about the anatomy of evil
Should you not make inquiries of the old broom
So well accustomed to probing the corners
Of men's hearts where evil grows and festers?
It is really not where you think
That we actually buried the ant.'

At this point, Ezenwanmadu upbraided Nwoye saying,
'A man who eats with kids may be smeared with oil.
I will not be the bed-ridden adult
Who eats soup made by kids.
Was it not the skunk that invited those who were not
Aware of its mother's death to first look at its mouth?
A child's first teeth are not examined with empty hands.

'Nwoye, the origin of a torrential downpour
May be hard to tell,
But there is nothing that happened on the treetop
That the hawk is not privy to.
It may be nice to heat up the stone
But how about its retrieval from the fireplace?'

Ebenebe said to Nwoye,
'Nwoye, should you ask the dog not to eat feces-
Are you going to eat it?
Is it not more seeming for the chicken to retrieve
The carcass of a fallen dog?
A hawk does not prey on its young.
Please, do not be like the spirit who went to kill,
Saw a corpse, and proclaimed that his job was done.
Nwoye, we do not pull the cheek of a child
Who is on the verge of crying.'

Then Nwoye replied,
'Men of Ezira,[11] I am truly sorry.
If the bush animal runs fast, we shoot fast.
Is it not he who touches something smelly,
That smells his hands?
A blind man may be lied to about
The color of a soup, but of its spices and herbs,
He needs no telling.

'I will not because of prolonged famine,
Claim that the head of a cocoyam
Is better than my mother's head.

All I say is that the dog that ate
Both cocoyam and yam is entitled
To a drink of palm wine and a battering rod.

'He who is found near a fruit tree
May be accused of stealing fruits.
A bad goat driven from the garden,
Goes to the yam barn.
Oftentimes, the dog that wishes to die
Refuses to acknowledge the smell of bad feces.
The child who refuses to take advice from an
Old woman, must be asked if he grew up with her.'

Then I addressed Nwoye saying,
'All these references to excrement irritate me.
Nwoye, the dog that eats feces says
It is well enough alone and need not be reminded
Of the good and tasty food.
Besides, was it not the cockroach that said
That its death in the jar of palm oil is a good death?

'He who was not there when a she goat is dissected
Asks if there was a baby in her stomach.

'Is a tree not best known by its fruit?
You are merely looking for reasons
To say that your hands aged before
They reached a hungry child's mouth.
The dog said that those who are serious about
Feeding it should leave the bone on the ground
And not worry about its fight with the spirits.'

I must have been shouting because Nwoye said,
'A shouter shouts,
But let he who displays that unruly talent
Tell if his voice is noisier than the gun.
Ezenwanmadu, if this child eats more breadfruit than I,
I will fry goat droppings for him.

The child who bit my fingers when I am feeding
Him roast yam raises questions as to which of
Us first learnt of that relish.'

Okonkwo promptly intervened,
'A man with a broken nose does not sniff.
Nwoye, if you must shop for stones,
You must learn to carry them.
He who fetches ant-infested firewood
Invites lizards to dine with him.
Nwoye, you were told that a fledgling
Is never known by its size.'

Nwoye then said in a more conciliatory tone,
'This child is probably a classic case
Of a man with a big head,
That does not know how to oil it.
When a rooster soils its feet,
It looks for a grassy land.
I will not be the first hawk to prey on a tortoise.

'This child hangs out in an abattoir,
He should be remarked.
Son of his fathers, I am sorry.
It is wrong to request a chair from the lizard
When I have not seen any upon which it is sitting.'

Then Ezenwanmadu spoke to me,
Imploring me to be more hospitable.
'A dog does not eat the bone
Hung around its neck.
The child who insists on eating alone
May be left to fight alone.
Son, please be more cordial to your fathers
Because we all know that it is rare that an
Unwitting strike of the knife severs the hand.'

Then I *said*,
'The dog that swallowed a crab
Is in serious thought.
When we harbor too many secrets,
The deaf man usually ends up hearing it.
O stranger, should I be forced to listen
To bad drums, is my head a drumstick?
The chicken said it knows how to catch snails
But that it has nobody to hold a basket for it.
But for its eyes, men would have tied
Firewood with this snake.'

Then Ebenebe spoke,
'The weak animal is advised to avoid
The forest of bamboos.
A man does not tempt a river that swallows boats.
But an old woman who chances upon new clothes
Often attends uninvited functions.
Yet, the frog being aware of their vast array
Of seasoned dishes, says it is scared of men.
'All men,' he insists, 'are like sneaky dogs,
They all eat chicken eggs.'

'Did we not advise that when a man
Reaches the land of ear cutters,
He must cut his or have them cut?'
'Still,' he added, 'a child is not beaten
According to the cost of his mischief.'

Then I *replied*,
'I know that if it does not rain,
It normally shines, but
When I shouted *o lo lo lo o*, did I ask it to rain?
I am like a chameleon,
I would not because the forest is on fire
Abandon my majestic ways.'

Then *Ezenwanmadu said*,
'Yes, but instead of a bite and a grimace
Should you not let the contents of the pot cool down?
Even then, let he who must play mischief like the hen
Learn to run like one, for its furious pursuers
Slip and fall, while the hen evades them,
With seeming effortlessness.'

Then I *said*,
'N*giga*, the fish receptacle, said it could not be afraid
Of fire and still choose the fireside to reside permanently.'

N*woye said*,
'Then let the tortoise know that we are tired
Of expecting it to have a baby.'

Then I *replied*,
'I have told you that a man beaten by a bee
Fears the housefly.
A child burnt by fire fears ashes.
Even then, when did it become hard to trace
The footsteps of the elephant?

'I have perceived that you are all women
Who trade in fermented oil bean,
You would know the one-eyed fly.
Nwoye, you especially would know
If a feathered fowl is sweating.'

'Aha, is this the case of the dissembler
Who desecrated the land
That seeks to protect the land from death?' Nwoye asked.

'No, Nwoye,' Ebenebe intervened,
'He said the palm fruit that falls to the ground,
Gathers a handful of grass.'

Then Nwoye said, rather impatiently,
'Well, let the squirrel explain who gave him
A roasted palm fruit.
If a chicken insists that it is drunk,
We might arrange a brief visit with the fox.'

Then I said to Nwoye,
'You talk like a kid who has not chewed his water
That does not realize that water has no bones.
I am like a creeping plant that fears no boundary.
Whatever I am fleeing from is significant.'

Ezenwanmadu pleaded,
'Nwoye, do not wash your hands
To crack kernels for the chicken.
I would not assume that the moon runs
Unless I have set foot on it.'

Nwoye said,
'About this child and proverbs,
I am reminded of a dog that enters a forest with a bag,
There will be no freshly laid feces left.'

Ebenebe laughed for the first time and said,
'Indeed, Nwoye, he who applauds a lunatic is a lunatic.
Indeed, this child and proverbs - if he whom I invited to dinner
Washes his forearms, is he asking me to fall
Into the river?'

Perceiving that they all meant well, I said finally,
'He who does not know that a squirrel is sick,
Let him look at its eyes.
Besides, is there any old dog that does
Not know he who sells bones?

'O mystery fellows,
I do not know why the vultures are gathering
When there has been no death.

When did I become a bush
That snails may be sought in me?
I am like a chicken, I would advise those
Who have heads to fight the war of sticks.
I am a dwarf, he who insists on breaking my fall,
Let him first break the fall of the land.'

'What?' Nwoye muttered.

'I am a dirty soap
With what will you cleanse me?'

'Son, we now have a *plenus* of fish eaters
Why not lower the fish receptacle?' Nwoye pleaded.

'Where lies a man, lies his spirit.'

'What?' Nwoye asked, pretending not to understand me.

'Nwoye, please listen carefully,
A good ear does not have a large span.
In a forest littered with dead birds,
Should you not look for a bird killer?
Where lies a slave, lies its oppressor.'

Finally, lachrymose and with cracking voice, I *said,*
'Fathers of their son,
I am like a tree that grew near the trail,
I got tested with much urine, phlegm, and
Newly acquired machetes.
And now, I have become the lamb in the ditch,
My tiny voice, my weak legs,
The impending visit from the leopard,
They all compound my anxieties.

'The tide has carried the newly hatched
Tadpoles out to the turbulent stream,
They will make fodder for the fish.

The stream has overwhelmed the aged frog.
The old owl is finally overburdened by the size of its head.

'How was I to know that a fire
Does not recognize who fetched it
And tenderly brought it to being?
Has it not left the pot to kill
The contents of the pot?
Has it not crossed the stream to kill a spawning toad?
And now only blinking awaits the eyes.

'Still, I am not settled about your intentions,
For that which is responsible for a wound
Is also responsible for its aggravation.
However concerned you may be,
Is it not he who fell off a tree, that feels the pain?
Frankly, I would ignore the flies on someone's lips,
I would not know if they dined on flies.'

Ebenebe said,
'True, sickness is best felt by its sufferer
But the brother of a lunatic feels his shame.
If the pumpkin does not grow for women,
What will pregnancy eat?
Son, it is always a good idea for the old woman
Who trips twice to stop and take inventory of her load.'

Then Nwoye said,
'If the mouth were shut,
Who would know the affairs of the heart?
Still, is it that the back feels cold or
That it could not find a fireplace?'

Ezenwanmadu said,
'The bees gather for urine
The flies for feces,
But why do wasps gather?
I tell you Nwoye,

The thorny bush that bothers a bird
Will surely kill a man.'

Finally I said to them,
'Fathers of their son,
We do not ask a bat to explain why it resents the daytime.
The tapster may not tell everything
He saw from the treetop.
But let the buttocks sit that will eat kola nuts,[12]
For the parcel may not be pinched
That may not be opened.'

Nwoye said,
'Let he who deigns to embrace a widow
Not rush the hug,
He may grab a flesh or two
We know where her husband is.'

'Nwoye,' Ebenebe said reprovingly,
'Did you mean to say that
A good trail is often revisited
Or that the lizard would love to sit
But for its tail?'

'No,' Nwoye replied,
'I meant to say that the old woman
Understands the predicament of
The male genitalia and its pitiful look
Has ceased to excite her.'[13]

'Shut up,' Ezenwanmadu said to Nwoye,
'If you must be a vulture,
You will be banished to the empty market place.'
'Son,' he said, 'the chicken retires
Not always on account of a full stomach.'

Then I said,
'Goodbye O mystery fellows.

However brief, the stomachs touch in a sincere hug.
I have truly felt the warmth of
Your souls against mine.
The sheep announced on the day of its birth
That nothing was too trivial to admire.
But, I would not disclose my admiration of a stranger
Until his mission is clearly and proven.'

Drumbeat!! Drumbeat!!

Endnotes

[1] A noisy bird.

[2] My "kinsmen" call the drummer Okonkwo, I call him Euhemerus.

[3] Supposedly, the house knife has more status than the farm knife.

[4] Referring to the habit of chickens to suddenly take off running without any apparent cause. The Igbos jokingly say that it must be that the chicken just farted.

[5] A town in Eastern Nigeria.

[6] The mortar carries food when upended by someone who is not skilled at using a pestle to marsh yam or cassava in the mortar.

[7] The Igbos have a tendency to personalize animals in their speech patterns.

[8] A palm fruit, different from a palm kernel, is studded with thorns.

[9] Although these men called me their son, this was the first confirmation that they might be kindred spirits.

[10] An unpleasant-tasting species of yam that preserves rather well.

[11] A precinct in Nimo. Nwoye, Ezenwanmadu and Ebenebe come from Ezira. Nimo, a town in Eastern Nigeria, is the author's hometown.

[12] Kola nut, a stimulant-containing nut, is the Igbo's equivalent of coffee or tea except that the offering of Kola nuts has near spiritual import. It signifies honesty, good faith, goodwill and a favorable disposition in the affairs between one and the other. That is why every gathering,   ceremonial or not, is preceded by the breaking of Kola nuts.

[13] Nwoye is well versed in proverbs and he can use them to great humorous effect. Nothing is a taboo to him. His manner of speech is not uncommon.

Chapter 9

Thoughts So Far Strayed

It is a day like
The day before,
And the day today after,
When mysteries continue to bewilder,
And the thinker
Stays awake in vain,
And the seeker roams
Endlessly and loses himself,
And futility is smeared
Upon the rewards of endless labor.

I had been lost in thought for days
Pondering; suturing up logical loopholes
And being quite blue.
I had refused to get up and about
Until the maze that was my thoughts
Was straightened out.
I had lost the will to smile.
I would sometimes rediscover what intense joy it gave.
Sometimes I smiled as if unworthy of its benefits.
My laughter was couched in aloneness,
A growing sense of vulnerability,
A feeling that even I can die.

Still I dreamt a cynical dream,
Subdimensionalized. God's whip cracking
My unbreakable back as both rider and horse
Rode off in search of new adventures.

'Here might I lie,' I sang
'Until the wind of hate is gone,
Then to continue my journey
To my maker's home.

'Here might I lie
Humming the tunes instilled in me,
In harmony with the music of creation.
Hence shall I arise
And return to my father.

'Here might I lie,
Pondering on this exile
From my home of unbounded beauty,
Longing for the day I shall
Again see the face of my God.'

But my resignation soon
Took leave of me,
And a troubled mind seized upon me

And I began to ponder upon the nature of man.

Have I not applied my mind
To the toils of men,
To all the businesses about which
His life is contained,
And have I not seen like the preacher
That all is futile and striving after the wind?

Why do men strive ceaselessly?
And grapple ceaselessly?
And conduct themselves
With arrogance, so palpable,
That it exceeds the proper manner of a
Psychological resource or even a subterfuge?
Surely it is ignorance, wantonly worn.

Why would a man need to be civilized,
Erecting structures and
Substructures in every facet
Of his life; in a feeble
Attempt to freeze uncertainties?

Are men not motivated by
Uncertainty, or the needs of men,
Or the uncertainty of the needs of men?
Are the needs of men not to make certain
That which is inherently uncertain?
Do men not toil
To eliminate uncertainty, or
To reduce it or to modify it?
Thus are men plagued by
The falsity of their truths or
The truths of their falsities.

O thoughts so far strayed
They cannot be rescued.
O that our irksome association

May be severed and calm
May fall upon these troubled waters.

Then I picked another strand of thought
And I tugged at it saying:
For whom is our world
That men may assume the right to kill?
Indeed, upon whose head should it lie,
To reorder his neighbor's house?
One whose house is disordered?

Not upon the head of an impostor.

Upon whose mind should it rest,
A vision of peace and calm
To a troubled world?
One whose heart is callused
Beyond the pleas of compassion?

Not upon the head of an impostor.

Upon whose head should it then lie?
Upon the sickled head of the moon?
Upon the blazing head of the sun?
Upon the twinkling detachment of the stars?
No. Upon our heads, all of us,
Upon us who esteem not our lives
Worthier than those of others.
Upon us who embrace not
A false foundation for
A universal order of peace.
Upon all men desirous of true freedom,
Relentless pursuers, hounders
After the quarry of universal justice,
Upon all men who wait not
To pay their dues of brotherhood.

I *had no doubt that*
I *had reached the realm*
Of endless loops!
At which time I felt the sound of drums.
It was Okonkwo the drummer-poet,
Accompanied by the mystery fellows.
They spoke in turns, starting with Ezenwammadu.

'May the sun arrive early on good days.
And may the remnants of evil die with the break of dawn.'

'Let the evil vulture
Be killed by the evil rain,' Ebenebe concurred.

'Let the wine that will bring quarrel
Spill in the gourd,' Nwoye added with his barrel voice.

The first voice addressed me saying,
'O son of Ezenwanmadu
What day is it?'

'Let the mad man be,
He knows his thoughts.' I replied.

Then Ezenwanmadu said,
'Son, a quiet corpse will be carried
Beyond its homeland.
Does sleep that affect the eye
Also affect the heart?
Let speech recognize its friends and stand.
Son, what day is it?'

'It is the thirteenth day of March
Several days after I met Alyssa.'

'O son of Ezenwanmadu,
Let sarcasm be the speechwork
Of the dull of intellect.

Besides, if strangers are polite
To one another, their acquaintance
Might be beneficial to both.
Therefore, let sarcasm be for its players,
But let your drowsy intellect
Be rustled up, to meet
My sincere inquiries; this I plead.

'O son of Ezenwanmadu
What day is it?'

'It is the sloth's day
A day of sleeping,
Like yesterday and tomorrow
Nothing to sing about.'

'Son, we associate in age groups not in wisdom,
Therefore, a child who eats words
With the finesse of an elder
May be required to repay his father's debt.
Remember that when men fall into
Trenches and crouch not
But keep one hand upraised
They might be pulled out.

'O son of his father,
What day is it?'

'A well fed stomach
Is a reluctant fire starter.
The mind is a bag,
Let everyone carry his or hers.
O mystery fellow,
I am not a thief; you are not my kinsman
That must bear my shame.'

'Was the man who would not learn from adversities,
Not asked to reincarnate

Before there were any one of those?
O son of his father, what day is it?'

'O mystery fellow,
Today as they say
Is yesterday's dream
And tomorrow's memory.
Indeed, like the day before
And the day after,
When the moon
Runs its course,
And the earth
Tumbles along its path,
And the sun
Blazes away with fierceness and rage,
And the stars
Dot the heavens in detached amusement.

'It is a day like
The day before,
And the day today after,
When the insects couple and mate,
And flowers bloom and die,
And predators prowl for prey,
And all creatures busy about their roles.

'It is a day like
The day before,
And the day today after,
When evolution steadfastly
Tiptoes its circular trajectory,
And the journey man finally
Reaches his destination,
And another lone wanderer
Sets out for parts unknown,
With randomness constituting the cradle
Upon which our world is borne.

'It is a day like
The day before,
And the day today after,
When mysteries continue to bewilder,
And the thinker
Stays awake in vain,
And the seeker roams
Endlessly and loses himself,
And futility is smeared
Upon the rewards of endless labor.

'It is a day like
The day before,
And the day today after,
When new classes are formed,
And alliances are shattered,
And bonds of friendship are broken,
And self interest continue to motivate
Strange bedfellows.

'Today, the impulses of
Class struggle and domination
Will parlay themselves.

'It is a day
Like the day before,
And the day today after,
When silver chords are broken,
And golden bowls are shattered,
And they return to him
That sent them and
To the dust that clothed them.

'Today, another leaf will fall,
And a new bud will emerge
Smiling at the sun,
And nature will dump upon itself,
And regurgitate a renewed self,

And they for whom the deceased
Shall open the sour pot of death,
Will convulse before its putrid face.

'Today, another will conceive violence,
And another's dream slips through the cracks
Of an unwieldy system,
And men of profit will lie awake, scheming away.

'O mystery fellow
That through time is lost,
Today is like yesterday,
Like a thousand years ago in essence,
And all else is frivolity,
Inconsequentiality, and mere sand.
Therefore, this day is this day,
A unit projection of itself in
Infinite dimensional space.'

At *this point* Nwoye *interrupted,*
'Is this the case of a man that was asked
To spot his burial ground, that wanders forever?'

'Nwoye,' I replied, 'in the dance
She excels in, an old woman is hard to tell.'

Ezenwanmadu continued,
'Son, I take it then
That you prefer not today
To a thousand years before
Or a thousand years today after?'

'O mystery fellow,
Indeed, a man is constituted
In time and space and
Substantiated with dirt.
Thus a man is fully defined
By the times in which he lives.

Since time is invariant,
Then all men are men;
Each generation distinguished
By the festoonery of the times
In which they lived.

'I ought to accept this day
And live it to the fullest.
I ought not prefer
A thousand years before
Or a thousand years after.
I ought not celebrate
Any time but the present.
Of myself, let the finest
Music be played and
Let me be inebriated
By the wine of my joyous
Embracement of me, myself.

'O mystery fellow
Whose concern I perceive,
I ought to celebrate myself but
All I see is the circumspection
Of planners of war.
All I perceive is the ambience
Of a place of mourning,
And the screechy malevolence
Of iron and aluminum,
And alarm sounding tocsins,
And war cries bodied in every face.
War, that outrage against humble men!
And I am surrounded by much
Hate, sorrow and violence.

'O mystery fellow
It is morning yet
On victor's day.
Ruddy slops of vitriol,

Prancers in victory dance,
Jubilant cries of a conquering army,
Acrid taste of defeat,
Adrenaline's surge of joy,
Triumph of one truth over another,
Hard won battle, sweet victory
That follows upon
The heels of a bitter fray ,
Verbal unguents of the general,
Sere humor of the President,
Sequins and medals of honor,
And girls of war. Assignations.
Trappings and emoluments of war,
War! Outrage against humble men.
Would a day, were a day
Without its impulses impelling
The wheels of blood.

'I see passions of anger
Loosened on the streets,
And children enacting
Revolution in the classroom.
I see trauma after trauma,
Minds callused to compassion
And mercy that has lost its virtue.
I see hounding dogs
That cannot hear their masters,
And death riding the gale of anarchy.
Indeed, I long for the
Frivolities of a different time.'

'Son, were you not taught
That the frivolities of today
Are decomposable to those of yesterday,
And your mind should rise
Above the mire, bog and dross
That your environment constitutes,
And thus celebrate yourself

Separate from the times
That brings you sorrow.'

'O mystery fellow,
Such ability belongs to minds edified.
Besides, how about the joy
That belongs to gregariousness?
What festival is there that
Was marked by one celebrant,
That was not greeted with contempt?
I desire that all men celebrate themselves.'

'Son, is that all that ails you?'
Ezenwanmadu asked understatedly.

'Surely, O stranger, you know
That the ills done to a child reside
Forever in its memory.
I am solely afflicted in spirit
For reasons that I am yet to learn.'

'Son, what spasms of emotions
Have gouged your glands,
And caused your tears to flow in rivulets?
What, O son of his father ails you?
For the spirits are disquieted by
Your foreboding sense of despondency.
Why would they that crouch fall,
But they standing on weak limbs,
On slippery grounds, strut with
Disgusting abandonment?

'Howcould a trap snare the wind,
Or a pride of lions be lacking in confidence,
Or the fish be bothered by the cross-current,
Or an eagle the convolution of the wind?
What ails Agubanze's son, what ails you?
For the oil bean tree does not bear breadfruits.'

'O mystery fellow,
Does the grass cutter run in the day for nothing?
Can smoke be buried?
Can the corpse be concealed from the ground?
Would the pottery break that was not touched?
Were the goat not hirsute,
Would its sweat not be easily perceived?
But then, solely my business surely it is.
But if you must insist,
Then be it known that
I have seen the black station
And its contents are laced with deep sorrow.'

'Go on son of his father,' he urged,
'The eyes are never weary of seeing
Nor the ears stranger to hearing.'

'O mystery fellow,
Willie had a bad song.
It was no song of love.
It was like a bad song composed by
A benevolent spirit, in a remote place,
Upon seeing human cadavers,
Human flotsam of a terrible wreck.
It was like a song rendered by
A mourning bird, no virtuoso itself.
It was like a duet composed by two orphans,
Both feeling the need to commiserate the other.
There was defiance, but it was human.

'Hark! Sad songs of defeat.
Hark! The piercing sighs of victims of perfidy.
Hark! The groans of a woman in travail.
Like the wailing of a mother,
An African mother, who returned
Smiling, graceful, with food and all,
To an empty house, victims of inhumanity.
Her children had been abducted by slave traders,

And the villagers by now accustomed
Gathered around, wondering,
Whose turn next time around.

'Can a harpooned dolphin
Pull on the chords of justice?
With an arched back, it reminds
Nature to adjudicate on the
Suppression of one creature by another.
What plea O falcon
To your favor by the falconer?'

'Son weep not, soul brother,
Is change not the only
Certainty to be encountered?
And life and death,
The being and not being,
Is the funnel through which
Change is poured.[1]
But one thing is clear,
According to the wind sowed,
So is the harvest of the whirlwind.
According to the firewood gathered,
So is the burden of its delivery
To the homestead.
According to an honest effort,
So is an honest reward.
And all else is the self-centered
Attempt to manipulate
The outcome of certain change.

'Son, reflect on a thousand years ago.
Wait; project if you could on
A million years hence.
Think of how many momentous events
Have been and shall be the
Outcome of the determinism of change.
Think of how many stars

Have fallen through the void
Of the universe, and what
Splintering explosion when
They finally hit its floor.

'Wait, reflect on the past again.
Think of how many helpers
Have become helpees.
Think of how many hyperactive limbs
Have frozen into the rigidity of rigor mortis.
Think of how many beautiful women
Have melted into the puckeredness of old age.
Think of how the squirming delight
Of a woman's tender limbs
Shall someday lapse into the
Arthritic despair of her old age.

'Wait, reflect on the past
And the future together,
Reflect on their co-determination,
See how the present convolutes
Between the past and the future.

'The brooding hen would scratch *frontwards*,
Then backwards, and implore her chicks
To compare the future and the past.
Such is the lesson of life,
That men wrestle in vain against time.'

Then Ebenebe spoke,
'O son of his mother
May peace rain upon you.
May the fire that burns within you
Not use your organs for faggots.
The Iroko tree stands tall,
Distinguished from his fellows,
Scraping the garment of the cloud
And daring the sun.

He who must be like it
Must be prepared to take some heat.
With immense branches
And outstretched ramparts,
It dares the sun god
To a wrestling match.
With strength of arms freely exhibited,
It demands to hug the heavens.
The climber looks at it
And loses his heart in dismay.
And the bees that nest on it
Are safe from seekers of honey.

'Son of his mother,
I urge restraint.
A sensible man does not
Kill a snake in the dark.
The crab boasted of how
It swam the mighty seas,
And survived many a cataract,
Yet it ended up in the widow's pot.
A child who must avenge
His father must be adequately prepared
Or he will fall to the same assailant.
The young ram that must go
On a challenging binge,
Must first ensure that his horns
Are strong enough.
The child who is learning to climb
Must be a bundle of abundant courage.
The chicken that attacks an anthill,
Must have swift and sure wings.

'Son, heed the lesson of the ants,
Consistent strivers, diminutive,
Yet unparalleled concentrators of will.
'Unity is strength,' says the ant
'Show me the universe to lift

And I will show you the collective
Will of my numerous kindred.'
Neither be like the winged termite
Who as an upstart emerged,
Too far ahead it flew,
And came crashing into the frog's mouth.
And then, they cannot have tried their best
If they come not exhausted,
Agape, with tired eyes.

'Son, always hang your baggage
According to your reach.
Were you not taught that modesty
Is a great attribute?
The ordinary and modest man
Is like a piece of cork
That would never sink
In the watery turbulence of life.

'Recall that okra is about the only
Fruit that did not come to maturity
Before it was plucked up.
Supposedly a thing of distinction, yet it cries.
Adequately fortified with palm oil,
Fish and pepper, it says,
'May my slimy consistency remind
You that I was plucked up
In the midst of my days.'
May despair not consume you.
Like one loved by the gods,
May you not be separated from
The fullness of your days.

'Whatever you do,
Bear in mind that the deaf ear dies
When the head is cut off on its account.'

Then Nwoye spoke,
'O free bird of the same breeder's stock
So you met Alyssa several days before?'

More srprised than amused, I answered,
'Nwanza, the tiny bird, broke a twig
And declared that this year must be it.
Yes, but solely my business, surely it is.'

And he said,
'O free bird, would you make her feel
The pressure of your crotch?
Indeed, how hot can a groin
Get in these times?
How hot can it get,
When all the heat is consumed by the brain?

'A woman pregnanted standing up
Gives birth to a mad child.
No wonder your generation is full of
Weak and mad children.
For a restless mind pays limited attention
To the exigencies of copulation.
And yet were there times
When all priorities were,
The perpetuation of the human species.
When putting all else aside,
A man deposited himself
Unreservedly in the woman's body.
For the business of copulation
Be not too busy.
For after all, the wherewithal for procreation
Is the sum of all of man's efforts,
And amoral love is its illegitimate justifier.
I have spoken.

'I am Nwoye Akubue,
I am the free bird,

I am the legend of the market place,
I am the constant maker of songs,
My music flows even in flight.'

The Ezenwanmadu said to Nwoye Akubue
'Surely O Nwoye,
You know that there is a time
To tap palm wine and a time
To be lost in its exquisite organoleptics?
Surely, this child knows that he who bespouses
A woman from Asaba,[2]
Must equip his boat for night journey.'

And Nwoye *said to me,*
'O free bird, should it be said?
Should it be said of you,
That in your springtime
You were diverted by
An armor that ought not be fulfilled?
For the genius of a man in love
Is channeled into the
Labyrinthine of a woman's
Cryptic ways and been
So tenuously spread, it loses its vitality.
For indeed:

'Where is genius directed?
There, where love doth flow
And led by a heart inclined,
To surrender to fate unknown.

'Where is genius directed?
There, where men of might dare not,
Where mysteries doth stall,
And mellowness seeps into our minds.

'Where is genius directed?
There, where sonneteers doth bask

And lovelorn hearts are left
To roam freely in the tunnel of love.

'Under the serene glow of twilight
They play it out,
Songs of yawning,
Deep sighs of joy
In the bliss to come,
Musical geniuses of all sorts
Inspired by the wakefulness
Of indulgent fantasies.

'O fellow free bird,
The oft trodden road
Does not grow grass.
Have you woven a basket
Of fantasy around her?
Have you adorned it
With garlands of tropical devotion?
Have you begun to experience
The gawkiness of a man in love
Who looking at the powerful
Erection he spots feels
That it alone can burst through
The fortified walls of an estate?
Have you reached down,
Felt the swooshing of blood,
And feeling so mighty
Agree that surely,
That is a worthy subject
Of your swan song?'

Then Ezenwanmadu upbraided Nwoye saying:
'Have I not told you that
There is a time to be excused
Of the languor of a newly wed
And a time to busy about the farm
To retain your bride's respect?'

And Ebenebe said,
'Shut up Nwoye, he is only a child.
We do not eat yam seedlings
Because we are starving.
When the string that ties a parcel tangles,
The parcel will surely open.'

At which Nwoye replied,
'The lizard that climbs the
Iroko tree is no longer an adolescent.'

And Nwoye continued,
'O freebird, looking at a newly hatched
Chick, you would think she would
So surpass her mother in beauty.
Looking at the rate at which Nwanza[3] grows,
You would think she would surpass
Her mother in size.
Do not be like the adolescent male
Who looking at his new found
Source of pride promises
To someday show up his father.

'Do not let things that drool rule you,
Or things that moisten up hold your sway.
For many a mighty man
Has gone the way of passion,
And found her wily ways
Too hot to handle.
It is true that certain male spiders
Give up their lives for passion,
But it is equally appropriate
That hardly any poet have sung
Of their heart moving devotion.
And I, Nwoye Akubue, will not
Be the first, or so, until
I am so inspired by as yet
Uninterpreted keg of palmwine.

'O free bird,
Love is a powerful tool.
It is a ship of voyage,
And many voyagers have boarded
Her to their own peril.
For love is like the open mouth of a lion,
The imprudent grasshopper that hops in
Must proceed with extreme caution.'

Drumbeat! Drumbeat!

So saying, the drumbeat faded
And with it, the mystery fellows.

Endnotes

[1] When death traverses this funnel, it is life and vice versa.

[2] A town on the banks of river Niger.

[3] A tiny bird.

Chapter 10

Song Of Love

If but a moment,
Let me smell your breath again.
Let us lay whispers in subdued light.
Let your tender breasts cushion
My wilding thoughts.
For this, our love begs description,
For which we have let out Wordsworth
And other poets in that frivolous pursuit.

Six months had elapsed
Since my last encounter with
The mystery fellows.
By now my romance with Alyssa
Had blossomed, teetered,
And ran its strange and powerful course.
In a fit of nostalgia, I sang,

'If I die,
In true memoriam,
Keep my songs.
Should I live on,
Show me off with joy and pride.
For on this day I proclaim
That before and after you,
My heart has known no greater joy.

'Sunshine at winter's dusk,
A purveyor of sunshine
Cannot keep it from herself.
Did we not sing on the day of vows:
'May our days of love be long,
May it rival the tortoise
In perpetual youth and
Ascend with the fowls in rejoicing.
At dawn, may our outstepping be
Attended by the flower of joy,
And at dusk, upon our instepping,
May our love be renewed like the
Returning moon.'

'Sweet, perfect harmony,
Lose me in your moist redolence.
Surround me with the aroma of your love.
May it be the levitating mist upon which
My pains will take flight.
Let your lusty and watery
Embraces ever attend me.

'If but a moment,
Let me smell your breath again.
Let us lay whispers in subdued light.
Let your tender breasts cushion
My wilding thoughts.
For this, our love begs description,
For which we have let out Wordsworth
And other poets in that frivolous pursuit.

'Would Wordsworth not reply,
'A shrub is not climbed,
Men walk around it.
The heart, not the genitals,
Is the proper equipment for love.
For beauty not properly loved, constrains.
And need creates pleasure, breeds lust,
But true love transcends all need.'

'In spite of all the days gone by,
In spite of all the emotional dross
That has been dumped within,
I look inwards and find you
An outstander, above time and will,
Above all else, pain and joy,
You are the white beacon
Conspicuously set, and all who enter
Assume the guise of trespassers
As you smear lethargy upon
Their gallant efforts.

'Softly, Alyssa, the moonshine sings.
For us birds an egg was laid,
From yesterday's whispers,
A bond was born.
Now have we found our quest,
For its season, now gone, was in.
'Yea, we have our joy still
But the rejoicers have gone;
Such is the anomaly that troubles the soul.'

Chapter 11

The Will To Love
Is Not Strained

I have come to present my bare buttocks to the ant,
To dispel the myth of its deadly sting.
But I never reckoned with the cruelty of these ants,
They seek out the tip of the anus.
I have come to experience racism,
To confront it,
To pass through it,
Be scarred by it,
Thus performing my rite of passage.

Supine and engrossed in my
Unctuous reflections, I was interrupted
By what had now become the familiar
Sound of Okonkwo's drum,
And the presence of the mystery fellows.
By now it had become clear that Okonkwo
Was the stage setter, who plunging into his art said,

'To each is the consequence of his deeds,
But a feces without a tip
Is of diarrheic buttocks.

Titi nko nko tim!

'If urination were easy,
Let the chicken attempt it.

Titi nko nko tim!

'The palm fruit that fell into the soup pot
Boasts that it has finally reached home.

Titi nko nko tim!

'He who swallows a handful of *foo-foo*[1]
Has broken the pot of hunger.

Titi nko nko tim!

'The hands of a tired man,
Are most conveniently laid on his knees.'

Titi nko nko tim!

Picking up the cue, Nwoye said sarcastically,

'The mushroom knows its guilt
For why else would it not let her waist
Touch the ground?

If the Guinea fowl's head shrunk
Because it catered to its kin's problems,
One wonders how it intends to solve
The problems of the world.'

Ebenebe agreed, saying,
'A braying sheep that invites the lion
May not run.
A man outrun by snails
Should not eat meat.'

Then I retorted angrily,
'A gun is not insulted in its face.
Besides, is there any manner of rainfall
That the earth is not aware of?'

And Ezenwanmadu spoke, saying,
'Brothers, it is no great achievement
To jump over a dwarf.
When a man is not dead,
We do not discuss what killed him.
The man with rashes,
Does not scratch his eyeballs.
It is only fair
That hunger visits the wealthy.
Son, remember that a trench is not covered
By a single hand, that okra does
Not outgrow its owners.

'Son of his father,
Why have you taken maniacal
Residence within yourself,
Spending countless hours
Reenacting dependencies and
Have let your days slip in idleness?
Are you not aware that sleep that
Lasts a market week[2] is death,
Or that the palm kernel cracker invites the chickens,

Or that anxiety magnifies today's sorrows
And drains tomorrow's strength?'

'Father of his son,
A man who forsakes his dreams forsakes his life,
I have not forsaken my dreams.
A cow wagging its tail is not dead,
I am still wagging my tail.
Rainfall does not wash off the spots of a leopard,
I am still a spotted leopard.
Indeed, I am eager to know my enemies,
I am merely pretending to be dead.

"Let me be for
I sing of what I know.
I sing of what I have become.
I sing of the victim that I am.
I sing of the icy hands of hatred
That rest on my back.

'When I retreat to the desolate
Evanescence of memory blank,
To obtain a reprieve from slight and slant,
There joined by the throbber strong,
Joined by the drooling thruster
Without whom all pleasure is lost,
I bask in ideality,
And ruminate on visions of ecstasy.

'Father of his son,
Let me stay bottled up,
Alone in my orality,
Alone in my imagistic world,
Alone, where rationale is one that heals,
Where baseless contrasts are not allowed,
And the will to love is not strained.

'When I retreat to the desolate
Evanescence of memory blank,
To avoid the dissipation of creative vigor,
To allow my mind to look into itself,
To repress the ills by which I am flustered,
To glue up my fragmented self,
To inflate my shrunken spirit,
To skim away all floating gook of self-doubt,
To rouse up a dying psyche,
And to dispel the fog of death consciousness;
From that insular vantage point
I wage a gallant struggle against self-attrition.

'Father of his son,
I must stay bottled up,
Alone, here, where I am my own physician
Humorist and lover,
Where I, myself, must heal
And the will to love is not strained.'

Then Nwoye said,
'Son all that bombastism is from
Too much association with white women.'

'Nwoye, you of the palm wine breath,
Merely did I state that in my state of mind,
All that is ridiculous is well liked
And shall have an easy time indeed.'

'O free bird of the same breeder's stock,
You are mad,' Nwoye concluded.

Drumbeat! Drumbeat!

'*M*ay the wings of the bird crack
That will not share a perching platform.'

'*The child who will quarrel with his father's wife,*
Requests for palm oil with which to eat palm fruit.'

Then Ezenwanmadu continued,
'Son, did the lizard not land
From the giddy heights of the Iroko tree,
Whereupon it looked for laudatory exclamation,
And not receiving any it said,
'I dare any stunt man,
I congratulate myself?'

'Son of his father,
Is man not his greatest admirer?
Besides, should you not eat
The eye of the mongoose
And trace the footsteps of the snake?
Should you not trod the thorny road
And with patience bear the pangs of hunger?
For the kite may eat what it may,
The vulture will eat the dead kite.

'Son, we agree, that it is pathetic indeed
And unparalleled, a tragedy of history,
That the children of Izaka
Turned against us that harbored Izaka.'

'Izaka,' I thought, 'Izaka.'
Nonplussed.
No words were consolation enough.
Turning sideways,
My mind drifted away saying,

'Wretchedness and emotional destitution
Are life's true quality and a free will
Tied to a mystical golden gate,
In the vast desolation of the breeder's mind
Swinging back and forth, guarding
And preventing nothing it seems,
Yet is the universal timepiece
That ushers in history, directing lives
From epoch to epoch.

'See how he rejoices in his great catch,
Yet must the angler be deemed foolish
Who glorifies his skill and does not mourn
The haplessness of the mighty fish.

'From that inner recess of being,
Of utmost privacy and inviolability,
That edifice that dignifies a self,
Proceeding from that deep cavern
Of individuality, it is strange that
Dreaming has become a privilege.

'Wild and coarse,
Full of fatuous sensuousness,
Like a bad weed proliferating unbridled,
Like a mass of unwantedness, borne by hurricane,
Is the dream of the privileged fool.
In contrast, from great men emanate
Manifolds, purity of vision, distinguished
Echoes, vivification of noble intent.
And still from the not too great,
Battered, afraid and downtrodden,
Emerge dreams, dreamt one at time,
Stripped, layer after layer of their
Creative geniuses, scared of their reverberations.

'How fitting that all may make
Bubbles of their own dreams.
In ones or multiples thereof,
Watching them soar, gently transported
By the compassionate breadth of nature,
Wafting freely in the midst
Of our mutual and collective efforts,
Popping it up if they would or
Letting it live out its span
Designed and etched upon the
Tabloid of universal laws.

'Dream if you would,
Of the status of a god
Or of fellow men.
Aspire if you would,
To be kings or servants.
Dream if you would,
Of nothing, no aspirations,
Just you, existing and satisficing.
Let your equipotent mind
Sway you where you will,
And plead not the inauspiciounesss
Of any circumstance.

'I, to the class of lesser greats
I belong, by necessity,
To whom no subliminal visions may be adduced.
I, who must proceed
From one mundane thought to another
Lamenting nature's colorful tinge,
Meddler, affecting the depth and clarity
Of my visions.

'Hence, from my laminae of dreams,
Stripped one after another
By the restraining influence
Of an unwholesome tradition,
I refuse to tread on the path
Matched by hero's past
Since my song is destined to be a cacophony
That would be sung by me alone.

'With that vestige of what ought to be,
I dream of this interminable orgy
Of love, compassion, affiliation;
Of the day, when beyond the barriers of flesh,
We would behold the inner light in us,
Aglow with passion, affirming our oneness,
Desperately seeking to be released

From the misery and insecurity
Of our sorrowful bondage.

'I dream of that day you would perceive
The outpouring, unstinting, of love,
And loosen the rein of your own
Inward captivity, and become with me
One family of earthlings in love.

'I dream of that twitch,
That smile, those lighted eyes
Constant reminder, that not being
Capable of much on our own,
We will someday be heroes together,
Jointly sung, as we seek to
Improve upon the sacrifices of heroes
Who have been this way before us.

'So, azygous, without partner or mate
Let me conjure up my dreams.
I, an alien to my planet of birth,
A stranger to my own mother,
Painfully reminiscing about
A dark and turbulent past,
The pains our mothers felt,
The terror that seized our fathers,
In history's darksome youth,
When culture lost its innocence,
And men thrilled by the exhilaration
Of catastrophe sought passionless eloquence.

'Thus, the past indicts the present
Bemoans the future.

'And so, like a caged bird,
Of traditions steeped in stereotypes,
I cry continually for my freedom.
With songs couched in defiance,

Without the bondage of rhymes and meters,
I versify freely to my taste,
Reveling in imagism,
Manufacturing words at will.
Let my libido, like my verses
Spawned freely to my taste, not bear
The repressive scars of
Intellectual starch and rigorism.'

Then Ebenebe spoke up, asking,
'Between tears and laughter
Which is foreign to men?'

'Tears and laughter are like palm kernels,
There is no tribe without their eaters,' I answered.

'Then let your soul be moved
To the depths of compassion
When it should, and then to
The heights of a mighty rejoicing
When it should so that
You may be one with all men.'

'Father of my mother,' I yielded,
'Has righteousness not lost
Its cloak of virtue?
Poets have hoisted amorous love
With lofty sayings.
Yet empathy is true love,
That which we were enjoined.
And all else is sweat, vapor
Bad breath and animalism.'

Nwoye laughed and the drummer mocked:

'The preacher from Louisiana
Remonstrated against amorous love
Yet dwelt with the prostitute
In her lair.'

Being more lightly spirited
And somewhat invigorated, I sang,

'Pale, like a plant in drought,
Like a hero without a song,
Besmearer of the beautiful,
Acid laden cloud, ominously looming
Above the greenery of nature's love,
Mighty hands, mightily clasping
The lonely and the faint hearted,
Should you foolhardily demand
Obeisance from me, strong and terrible?'

Then sitting upright and gazing upward,
I thought,

'Who can discern their circuits,
The stars, who guides them in procession?
Who can match their grace in dance
Or understand by what thoughts they smile?
When their rage is unleashed,
Who can restrain them?
The fierceness worn by the sun
Who clothed him?
Only he the breeder, greatly to be praised.
To him, I pledge my undying love,
To him, let all obeisance be,
My advocate, my tribune, with whom
I alone have become a majority.'

And the drummer drowned my thoughts
Beating in a vigorous up-tempo, he went:

'The snake that bites the tortoise,
Bites a rock.
The rain that falls on a rock
Merely bathes the rock.'

I *continued*,
'Still, rebels we remain
In your midst, like the wind,
We cannot be grasped, we,
Of Ezenwanmadu, scions,
That cannot be made afraid
Like a hopper on the grass
Without our heritage to celebrate,
Our venerable past, that cannot be mocked,
Nor sieved, nor tainted, our humanness
That cannot be peeled.

'Still, rebels we remain,
Proud and vastly so
Whose songs shall be heard
And loudly too,
Whose destiny shall be ours
Rightfully to uphold,
To embellish as we deem fit
As our dreams foretold.'

Ezenwanmadu cleared his voice,
The drummer stopped beating.
Clearing his voice again, he said,
'Son of his father,
What are you doing in a strange land?
Does a child visit his father's creditors?
Does a child afraid of slavery
Leave his father's stead?'

'Father of his son,
I was told that a dog that wanders far
Eats well-oiled feces.
It is not because of the love we have for kites
That we forbade women from eating them.
A fire starter does not swallow
Smoke with pleasure even though
He knows that smoke precedes a fire.

'I have come to present my bare buttocks to the ant,
To dispel the myth of its deadly sting.
But I never reckoned with the cruelty of these ants,
They seek out the tip of the anus.

'I have come to experience racism,
To confront it,
To pass through it,
Be scarred by it,
Thus performing my rite of passage.

'I have come guided by
Unflinching belief in equality,
On a voyage of self-discovery,
Have I come, only finally to realize
That all men, although created equal,
Are not to be equally regarded.'

'Son, how may you be regarded?'
'I am black,' I muttered.

'Son of his father,
How may you be regarded?'

'Father of his son,
I may not be regarded at all.
I may be regarded less.
I must not be regarded equally.
My history may be that of
Endless voyage in self-actualization
And the story of my life
Studded with tales of thwarted dreams.

'I am a landless dweller
On the earth of our fathers.
Like an uprooted stump, I am
Destined to shrivel and die.
Like a barren woman,

I may die, not leaving a trace of me
I may die in my unfulfillment
I am black.'

Then Ebenebe spoke,
'Son of his mother,
That a housefly has entered the mouth is one thing,
That it should be allowed to enter the stomach is another.
A wayfarer is advised to carry along his spices
In case he is served cocoyam.
Still, a child who is afraid of slavery,
May not leave his father's stead.
The man who knows no etiquette
Invites questions as to his birth place
For how could he tell the sacred grounds,
Or know which idols must be lifted with both hands?
It is never that the hot piece of yam cannot be chewed,
It is always that the teeth could not find a way.
Besides, what one is, one is.
We are regarded, as we regard ourselves.'

'Father of my mother,' I replied,
'The cockroach does not know which way to crawl
Without offending the wall gecko.
I held my speech
The times I could,
They said, 'This nigger is unfriendly.'
Then I laughed and talked
And showed a merry face, they said,
'This nigger is not serious.'

'The nigger laughs last,
He may not set an undesirable precedent.
But when he laughs last,
They say, he did not understand the joke.'

'Then laugh in the middle.'

'A genuine laughter is hard and long.
When we of the rain forest laugh,
It is like an explosion
That polarizes the particles of air
And sends a current of life
Eddying and dissipating in the
Greater atmosphere.

'Father of my mother,
A good laugh has a long tail,
A last laugh is laughed short.

'Must a tiger shed its *tigritude*?
Is it not clear that when a man
Is bent on divorce, his wife's
Tasty soup will not sway him
One way or the other?
Am I not the unwanted stump
In the prairie that must be uprooted?
Like the night that bodes fear,
The grandson of ignorance, I am.'

Son of his mother,
'We asked you to build bridges not walls,
To be patient because a bitter drink
May leave a sweet after taste,
To remember that always, the sun
Shines first on those standing.
And why is it that many of your people are preparing to
Shave a man's head in his absence?'

'Father of my mother,' I replied,
'It is true that
A man who does not get his own piece of kolanut
Should first find out what happened to fingernails.
But they avoid us because in their own words,
'A person who allows his ex-slaves a handshake
Should be prepared for an embrace.'

Embracing us, they say, is too awkward to imagine,
Especially when it is not the females of our kind.'

'Son of his mother,' he said,
'When the worm fell from the rafter,
The chicken rushed up and pecked at it.
Looking up, the worm said, 'Madam
When did we become enemies?'
Is such the nature of race relations
That men have taken an instinctive
Dislike for one another?
Son, I would have thought that
The generation of the white man
That oppressed your fathers was gone.'

Okonkwo interrupted,
'The eagle is pretty
But that it eats toads.
Any offspring of a kite
Will always prey on the chicken.
Besides, the catapult with which a child
Killed a vulture was made by the adult
Fellow kinsmen, can there be justice for a goat
In the leopard's court?'

Then Nwoye spoke,
'O free bird of the same breeder's stock,
Is it true that you come from a land
Where the cock crows
Announcing the dawn of a new day,
And the red jungle rooster greets
Each emerging hen, unashamedly,
Uncompromisingly, with a plea for sex,
And not to be outdone
It sheds its life-giving force once,
Then gestures for more,
Cavalierly spreading its wings,
Establishing its dominance,

And when it is done,
It raises its head,
It looks to the east,
Then to the west, positioning itself,
And crows once again
In the direction of the scribes in heaven,
Reminding them to log in another entry
Of his awesome sexual prowess?'

'It is true.'

'Is it true that you come from a land
Where the widow's wealth is centered
On the fecundity of her female goats,
And a man is esteemed by the size
Of his yam barn, and a man's strength is
Attested by the rate at which he sets up
Mounds following the second new rain,
And a bride's worth is greatly
Enhanced by the taste of her melon soup?'

'It is true.'

'Is it true that you come from a land,
Sultry, of deliberate and harmonious rhythm,
Exemplified by the hesitant but rhythmical
Movement of the jungle tortoise,
Who having accepted the burden of a
Mobile home, has become
An epitome of tranquility and equability?'

'It is true.'

'What happened to the ways of your fathers,
When men were loath to scar the soft tissue
Of nature with mechanized monstrosities,
And dutifully gave back to nature
What it was, they took from it?'

Drumbeat! Drumbeat!

'There was water in the riverbank
Before the coming of the rains.
The dog's nose was cold before the harmattans came.'

'Nwoye, my fathers are like hunters
Who could not find their game
And elected to sleep in the forest.
They are like the foolish beggar
Who sought alms in the poor man's house.
Indeed, they are like the foolish wife
Who emptied all her water pots because
She heard a rumble in the sky; no rains came.

'For did not the white man say to my fathers
'My culture is preeminent,
I am the standard bearer,
I lead where you follow?'

Did not my fathers say to me,
'The white man's ways are to be preferred
It is contemporaneous to favor his ilk?'
And have I not seen the white man's ways

'And do I not cry today,
'What transcendental absurdities,
How has my years been wasted
In blistery pursuit of Western Education
And the values that brings life
Englutted in my permanent underdevelopment?'

'Of the poetry of our fathers,' they said,
'It was us who infused civilization therein.'
Of the crispiness of our minds,
They said, 'See the manifest refinement
Of our ways.'
What transcendental absurdities,

What splurge of cultural arrogance,
How vast the sum of them.

'O mystery fellows
How might a culture be judged?
By the harmony between man and man
And man's environment or by the
Disharmonies between these?
Every where I look, I see
Discord, greed and avarice.
And the pillaging of the environment
And stampedes with
Hooves provided by the fourth estate.

'And yet they say to me,
'It was primitive, those that sought peace.
Stress is to be desired, it engenders wealth.
Peace is to be lightly esteemed,
It cannot breed wealth.'
And yet, wealth begets not freedom.
Freedom by itself, being the sole
Denominator of the attainment of
A civilized state.

'That men are free to seek wealth
Implies not that men are indeed free
But that they are shackled by greed
As they wriggle like maggots
In a decadent substrate of power
Each seeking by his actions
To enslave the other.

'That men are free not to seek wealth,
Where wealth is the law is a false doctrine,
Contrary to the rules of nature.
Thus a society, founded in unbridled
Pursuit of gain and knowing also
That by the sociology of truth,

That equal opportunity cannot be birthed by legislation alone,
Is one where anarchy would latently reside,
Waiting until the floodgates are open
To unleash its powerful force
On the monumental testimonies
To the toils of men.

'Fathers of their son,
When the pie is frittered away,
Political freedom flies afar off.
Whose vision would then include
Democratic vistas
Actionable only on the heap of
Aggrandized wealth,
The resources of the
World being not unlimited,
Whose hands can restrain the crashing surge
Of totalitarianism's wave
When men can neither be kept alive nor free?

Drumbeat! Drumbeat!

'Those who have had a surfeit of kernels
Tend to lose their cracking stones,
Then they forget that a people's firewood
Cooks their food.
The hawk that kills two preys at once,
Does it carry a hunting bag?'

Endnotes

[1] Marshed yam or cassava, normally dipped in vegetable soup.

[2] Among the Igbo's, market weeks come in four day cycles.

Chapter 12

Before Ham We Were

If Ham was to us a progenitor,
Then Adam was a black man but paradise
Was never sought at Ojita, the navel
Once bearer of the umbilical chord
Through which heaven shed its contents on earth.
Ojita allured by its mystical limpidity.
There, where praise songs
We sang, of us, souls, free,
Aligned with infinite reality.
Who would then proclaim us accursed slaves?

The visits from the mystery fellow
Had a calming influence on me.
I knew that there was much more to be said.
One early summer night, I slipped through
And witnessed a most amazing fire works
In the sky. Presently, the drummer showed
Through, accompanied by the mystery fellows.

'The hornbill said it lived
When there was no heaven or earth
And elected to bury his parents on his head.'

Titi nko ti nko

'Let the gathering of men be eventful,
So long as no one dies.'

Ko titi koko ti koko ti ko

'O mystery fellows,' I began, interrupting Okonkwo,
'There had been a lightning in the sky
From one frame as far as the mind can tell
To another as far as the eyes can follow.
If there is a pageant of the gods tell on
If there is a stirring in their council, tell on.'

Then Ezenwanmadu said,
'O clairvoyance that sweeps light
Towards the territory of the mind's eye,
O what a foretaste of death divine,
O son of his father, beloved and loved,
You have seen the homecoming of Izaka.

'I am Ezenwanmadu,
Before Ham I was.
Ezenwanmadu of Aniedobe, son and legend,
Elucidator of mysteries.
Who would much to history harm?

Not we, who interpreted palm wine
Before Noah, before the Kushites,
And the Canaanites.

'If Ham was to us a progenitor,
Then Adam was a black man but paradise
Was never sought at Ojita,[1] the navel
Once bearer of the umbilical chord
Through which heaven shed its contents on earth.

'Ojita allured by its mystical limpidity.
There, where praise songs
We sang, of us, souls, free,
Aligned with infinite reality.
Who would then proclaim us accursed slaves?
We, the guiding light,
Watchtower of the night travelers,
Lighthouse erected on the crest of the earth,
Lodestar that guided the earth to civilization's dawn.

'Son of his father,
Who else but Izaka
Would to history harm?

'Izaka never meant well,' the oracles said.
'Beware of renegades of the council of gods;
Beware of men who despise discipline,' the oracles warned.

'We cursed the day that gave birth to him,
The constellation that announced his mother's travail,
And upon the soil, where he first set foot
No greenery shall ever mark or grow.

'The day he first landed with a thud
At the rain forest of Owa,
We sought out his limp body
And nursed him to health.
But later we cursed the grains of water

That balmed him,
And the advances in medicine that
Brought him speedily to health.

'We had proclaimed him a warrior of our caste
And bid him, dwell among us
Who were kept by Ani,[2]
And Aniedobe,[3] who interceded for us,
Scions of the gods, born of Ezira
Land of the brave warriors
Who sprinted with the gods
And made sport with diadems.
Mingling freely, in harmony
With all around us, men, gods and beasts;
And paradise extended before us
From horizon to horizon.

'From land to land,
Bounded by seas and mountains,
We sought palm wine
Accompanied by Nwoye
And his caste of interpreters,
And made merry among great branches,
And traced the currents of delight ,
Endless flowing rivers, renewal agents,
Symbol of our perpetuity.
We tamed nature as nature tamed us.
Between her and us was that mutuality,
An accord that none may deplete the other.

'Our cosmogony was simple.
All were of the gods,
From where we came
There we will depart,
In the abode of our ancestors,
Store houses of God's breath,
And from such a store house
We have come,

To relate the story of Izaka.'

So saying I was swept up
To behold a splendiferous assembly
Too overwhelming, too resplendent to relate.
No army has ever been so magnificently arrayed,
No senses swift enough,
No versifier skillful enough,
To capture the brilliance of this people.
For all that is color bright, pale
Before the people of paradise.

This was the ancient people of Nimo
Gathered in their plenary,
Men, women, beasts, elders,
Titled men and women, tribal groupings,
Musicians, dancers, craftsmen,
All fully accessorized.
A mild chatter, a vibrant animism,
And a pervasive current of excitement
Hung heavily in the air.

My breath was heavy with fear and anticipation
And my job, merely to watch
And the furrows of my mind held a silent prayer
To the God of Jacob,

'My light, my salvation, whom shall I fear
My life's stronghold, of whom shall I be afraid?
For fear stumbles before I, whose trust is in the Lord.
Even in the valley of death, no evil shall I fear,
For with your rod and your staff, you strengthen me,
Awash with the blood of your lamb, death have I conquered.'

Okonkwo must have sensed,
For he animatedly beat away,
No drummer could ever match Okonkwo's amazing flair,
His muscular tone that flailed at the drums,

Threshing pure music from skin and wood,
His squinty eyes holding an all-knowing glitter,
His pendulous head movement keyed
To the rhythms he made.

'The yam tuber that trembles never reaches a strange land!'
He declared.

Drumbeat!!! Drumbeat!!!

Endnotes

[1] A small body of water set in the middle of a dense forest where the first species of any kind descended from heaven.

[2] god of the earth, said to be enduring and everlasting.

[3] Son of Ezira. Chief Priest of Ani.

Chapter 13

People Of Paradise

This was the paradisiacal people
Of the rain forest.
This was the first prototype
Of actors delivered to the giant theater of earth.
This was the people of Nimo, thespians all,
Dwellers in the lush and flourish
Of the valley, wherein lies Ojita,
Surrounded by a luxuriant assemblage
Of botanical species, and by an exquisite array
Of animals, full supporters cast.

For the first time, I saw Okonkwo.
He was a most charismatic man
And he spoke fast and well.
Intensely personable, he wore a constant smile.
Before any words would swell in his mouth,
The crowd chuckled.
His words were accompanied by a deafening
Outburst of laughter.

Okonkwo was roaringly funny.
He knew and enjoyed it.
Even better than his showman instinct
Was the marvel he wrought with drums.
He was one of a few men who could
Simultaneously beat and dance to a drum.

With his drum wedged in his armpit,
And a drumstick in his right hand,
He would walk briskly back and forth,
His wiry legs and powerful things not evading notice,
Acknowledging their greetings,
Stopping momentarily to salute a person or group,
He would dish out a totally new array of beats
And possessedly dance away.

He would sometimes stop,
Lay his drums between his thighs
And giftedly blow them away
With an assortment of rhythms.

Nothing, however, drew more applause
Than when with the drum aloft,
Held way above his tilted head,
Body glistening with perspiration,
His husky voice intoned a verse or two.
Whenever the crowd became too noisy,
He would say, ' a large gathering that
Becomes rowdy, greatly favors the trickish.'

Okonkwo had not just come to entertain,
There was a sense of urgency in his strides.
Once I sought and made eye contact with him,
His eyes easily seared through me.
It was not a good idea.[1]

Turning to the crowd, he began,
'May no one die,
May we not lose their fellows,
For the chin is the meeting place
Of palm kernel and the breadfruit.
And when Adakada and Ebe are seated,
We know that the gathering of dwarfs is complete.'

The crowd agreed.
'The dwarf who slipped and fell,
Said he and the ground
Both had something to regret.
The short man who initiates a commotion
In the market place often jumps up
To enjoy its outcome.'

The crowd agreed.
'Go on,' they urged.
'The old man lifts his snuffbox,
He remembers the days of his youth.
A woman who acquires new clothing
Has reasons to be first in the market place.'

With each proverb that Okonkwo
Reeled off, the people cheered
And acknowledged his craftsmanship,
Sometimes with a wave of hands,
Other times with praise-name calling.
Then out of the corner of the assembly arose a woman,
Bedecked in dancing costume.
She ran from one end to the other
Taking care to acknowledge the elders.

She stopped in the center, did a few
Vigorous dance steps, accompanied
By a hearty applause. She was
Mgbankwocha, daughter of Otenyi, whose voice was
Said to be of the weather-beaten gong.

Turning to Okonkwo, she genuflected
And reminded him that although the sons of Awato
Were the best tree climbers of their generation,
That a scrupulous fruit picker
Does not descend from the treetop.

Clearing her voice, facing the elders, she said,
'When we see the shape of an issue,
We determine the shape of the mouth that will tackle it.'

The elders nodded their agreement.
Then turning towards the people, she said,
'No news slipped her ears.
No secret was safe with her.
Whatever she heard, she talked.
She, Nwabuno, daughter of Amafum,
She of the slippery tongue
Whose tongue was said to be anchored in slime.

'Killed in exasperation by Izaka,
She knew all of Izaka's lovers and talked.
Whatever she knew, she talked.

'Stories were her quarry.
Men who harbored vice shunned her.
She, with the upright of a secretary bird,
The regality of the magnificent eagle
And the voice of a thousand sure birds …
Whatever she heard, she talked.

'Her intellect was crispy and precise,
A pleasure, sometimes, inordinately so.

She, mother of the fourth estate …
Something about her poise
That reminded one of the elegance of the egret…
Yet was there some disquiet about her,
For she had the sore tenderness of a cat …
Whatever she heard, she talked.

'When Nwabuno says listen,
It is best to listen.
And often does she say listen,
For her head filtered
A massive load of information.
Nwabuno of the slippery tongue,
I salute you.'

Drumbeat! Drumbeat!

Then Nwabuno arose,
With all the histrionics she could muster.
Tall, firm, with penetrative gaze,
Imperious and regnant as might be
Expected. Suddenly, the assembly stilled,
Became quite pensive. There was an air
Of melancholic expectancy.
Nwabuno would say listen.

'Listen!' Pause. 'Listen!' Pause.
Building up suspense, she said,   .
'Good people of Nimo,[2]
This was a time
When the sky was the squirrel's ground,
And the lizards could be counted
One at a time and the trudging path
Wound around the giant breadfruit tree.

'This was a time
When men detested shallow elegance
And cultural innocence shone upon them

Like a starry night.
All men pulled from
The same end of rope.
With nature, they tugged not differently.
And men's minds were not affected
By the tumescence of arms.

This was a time
When men detested gain,
And hastened to pay their dues of love,
And there was little need for laws
That men of evil may be purged.
Men passed through nature
And nature passed through men
And neither resisted the permanence of change.

'This was a time
When trails were paved
By gentle but persistent
Trod of human traffic
And neither weed nor men complained,
But each shook hands and nodded
In mutual acknowledgement.

'This was a time
When peace was carved into every mind
And no oasis of pride was permitted.
Mounds were made to adorn,
Not to destroy.
Men and beast drank from the same hole of water.
It was paradise, as paradise should.

'Men milked not,
It was nature's will that each species
Drink of its own milk.
Men probed not,
It was not meant that men be
Acquainted with the affairs of the gods.

But men may vie for compassion,
For kindness was it of
Which status was made.

'Men growled not,
Violence was alien to them.
Emotions were never arrayed in rancor.
Mild and meek, they were never too
Strong to bend. Yet, they stood firm
And yielded not, but fended off
Strains of base desires; cupidity,
Flatulence and concupiscence
That sow discord in the community of men.

'This was the paradisiacal people
Of the rain forest.
This was the first prototype
Of actors delivered to the giant theater of earth.
This was the people of Nimo, thespians all,
Dwellers in the lush and flourish
Of the valley, wherein lies Ojita,
Surrounded by a luxuriant assemblage
Of botanical species, and by an exquisite array
Of animals, full supporters cast.

'Ojita was nature's greatest masterpiece,
The center of our lives.
It sparkled in our dreams,
And allured by its mystical limpidity.
Its breath-taking, pristine elegance
Etched its ambience on a beholder's psyche.

'But alone at noonday,
Who may visit Ojita?
Whose strong mind could withstand
That tremulous descent of reluctant leaf fall,
The fluttering of leaves,
The chorus of emerging buds,

The scurry of rodents,
Presences, again presences…
The laughing trees,
The whistling of solitary birds,
Tranquility broken by overreaching monkeys,
Eerie presences…
The beggary of *birdlings*,
Hurried steps in exit…
The rain forest that awes, mystifies and allures.

'He who visits Ojita at noontime
Desires the company of spirits.
There was Nwagu of Urukweluora,
He of the chronic back pain,
Then Isiekwe, the refractory apprentice to Ifezue,
The famous blacksmith of Ezira,
And then, there was Emenike of Uruezebaluchi
Who sought healing herbs at noonday.
They all died.'

Drumbeat! Drumbeat!

'Nwagu, Isiekwe, Emenike,
Were you not told that
The child who tempts a python
That has run out of rodents is foolhardy,
That an inquisitive chicken is soon
Covered with a basket?'

Drumbeat! Drumbeat!

'The salutation due an absent elder
Should be given to his empty homestead.'

Ti tim kpo tim kpo.

'S*alute a deaf man,*
If the earth does not hear your greetings,

The heavens will.'

Ti tim kpo tim kpo.

'For an act of charity
Is greater than a thousand incantations.'

Ti tim kpo tim kpo.'

The drums stopped in anticipation
Of Nwabuno's next speech,
Who acknowledging their respect
Motioned for the crowd to be seated.
Then walking between the rows and columns
Searching out remarkable members of the group
She said in a loud voice,

'People of Abba,[3]
Artful clothes craftsmen,
You wore your clothes inside out.
We asked and you said,
'A phenomenon is as easily defined
By what it is as by what it is not.
A thing of beauty, real beauty,
Must be admired from both sides –
The inside and the outside.'
Yes, we agree. Your philosophical
Instincts were awesome. But
It is not necessarily those
Who wear their cracking stones
That eat the most kernels.

'Nweke Otachala,[4] of Uruolioke,[5] whistler at dusk
We heard you. You preferred it small
And simple. We heard you.
You would rather the simple job with dignity
Than the high profile job with indignity.
We heard you. Merry on. Talented one

Who mortgaged his gifts to palm wine
You poetry drooled like saliva
From the corner of a voluptuary's mouth.

'Nwokolo, of Uruokokwe,[6] face of a thousand wrinkles
And permanently creased brows, I salute you.
What happened? Was it the fact that
You were laden with incongruities:
Severe penury and baldness?
Yet you heard when the elders said
That wisdom mitigates poverty.

'The poor man sometime sits like he is sick.
He is like a tortoise.
Show him an elephant's carcass,
And watch his spirited rush at its meat.

'A man dies when a man will die,
Obidigbo[7], the renowned tree cutter,
You too, son of Uruokokwe, I salute you.
A man who has an irresistible craving for meat
Is advised to first consider a piece of his own tongue.
You inherited all of your five brother's wives,
And married none of your own, I salute you.
We are still not settled
About the circumstances of your brothers' deaths
You, Obidigbo cut down the mightiest Iroko trees
And yet were killed by the falling branch
Of your brother's wife's pear tree,
What sweet irony!'

She paused, starring down at Obidigbo.

'A man who sires children by his brother's wife,
Sires children for his brother.
Seeing you standing by yourself today,
I dare say it is sweet justice.
Obidigbo Nwaebue of Uruokokwe, I salute you!'

Obidigbo, compactly muscular and combative.
Did not find things funny. He retorted:

'Nwabuno, an offensive mouth invites knives
To leave their sheaths.
It is true that the old broom knows the corners of a room,
And that the chewing stick knows
The intimate affairs of the mouth,
But a person who has never had a sore
Should not swear fealty to the housefly.
You, Nwabuno, you impress me as a bathing vulture would.
You would only end up becoming uglier.
A man marries you only because a rag might have its uses.
Nwabuno, you assume you know everything about everybody,
But be advised that the eyeball never rises above the eyebrow.
I salute you back if that is the edge you seek.'

'Obidigbo,' Nwabuno continued, sounding miffed:
'I do not assume...
I am the low flying eagle,
I see what every fowl sees and
I am the terrible hunger that visits even a king.
I know not the things that fear, I fear you not.
I am the tongue to your aching tooth,
My fixation on you is not to ease your pain.
A person who contends with a fool is a fool -
A fool worse than a liar whose bag is never full.
Only you would suppose that the tongue
Would be ignorant of what the mouth is chewing.
You may shout all you want, but remember
That the shrieking of the sacrificial fowl will not avail it.
We, the people of Nimo are like salt
We will not be infested with worms.

'Obidigbo, the world is a market place,
A man makes his purchase and leaves.
A bad deed too long ignored, becomes a tradition.
But as to the culpability of the mortar, we need no telling-

For why else is it bound to the ground?'

Sigh! 'Obidigbo, I salute you!'

An elder interjected:
'Nwabuno, we do not pour water into an already filled pot.
We elders are hill dwellers, we know how best to climb it.
It is true that the watching eye is the best narrator,
But we do not know of a swimmer who talks under water.
Be advised that the drummer does not lead the dance troupe.
It is up to us to decide how best to climb this fruit tree.
I have spoken.' It was Nwawelugo of Ebonato.

Nwabuno seemed too busy to listen, she continued:
'Uvoko,[8] son of Ezira,[9]
Land of the brave warriors
And of the laughing leopards
Who are not rattled by the quiver's haste,
I salute you and your flute as well.
We sought both your flute and dancing steps
At the funeral ceremonies of our elders.
I salute you.
Shall we again do the dance of monkeys?
One step on the ground, three steps in the air,
Or the dance of the water skater
Guided by silky surface tension?
If we must, keep your flute aside.
Let me not suffer the fate of Mgboye[10]
Who complained of chronic chest pain
Because you made love with the flute
Secured around you neck.

'Nweke Akujieze,[11] the reticent and cunning titled man
Of Ogwulugwu ana,[12] I salute you.
When you attained the ranks of the elders,
You actively sought to enjoy the perks
Of that esteemed office, I salute you.
Today, I might venture to ask you,

How come a man of your stature was not ashamed
To dance to the sound of pestles?[13]
I might also ask you, if he who has a piece of yam
Makes a bucket of sauce, what does he expect from
The yam farmer - a river of sauce?

'I might also ask you, Nweke,
If he who is invited runs to a feast,
What does he expect of the feast maker?
I salute you.

'Today, we recall your famous defense against Mgba,
Your mother, who charged you with willful neglect.
First, you said there was no easy way to conspire
To betray one's mother. We agreed.
Then you said that Mgba ate two pieces of yam
And complained she had no teeth,
Whereas those who had teeth ate none.
Then you said that the same Mgba
Who claimed she had no teeth complained
Of toothache when asked to look after your toddler,
Whereas she was not asked to bite her.
'I am a true testimony,' you concluded,
'That even a good man makes smelly feces.'

'Nweke, the old woman may look as if
No bride price was paid on her head,
But a mother is a mother.
When a cunning man dies,
A cunning man will bury him.
I salute you.

'Mgba,[14] mother of Nweke, daughter of Urumkpoke,
I salute you as well.
When we admire the molted skin of a snake,
We do well to also admire the stick that bears it.
A titled woman that will gossip
Usually paints her lips.

And yet who can forget your enthusiasm
At festival gatherings.
It was for you that it was often said
That an old woman who dances out of step,
Claims it was the step of a strange and bygone era.
We know that the old woman who has
A left over of food that she relishes
Often responds eagerly to greetings.
Mgba, I salute you.

'Aniebuemu,[15] son of Atukpolom,
The deliberate and omnivorous one, I salute you.
Your philosophy was as simplistic as it was instructive.
First you said that in the absence of yams,
One must convince oneself that cocoyam is yam.
Then you said that a poor man does not eat the eye of a bull,
For the poor man's goat is his cattle.

'Then you were fond of saying that
That which is both plentiful and precious is rare.
About why you were so deliberate, you would often say
That a chicken fills its stomach, one grain at a time,
And there was nothing up that was not down.
About why you were generally misunderstood,
You would cheerfully answer that the breath
Of the early morning tapster, confounds the flies.
Aniebuemu, I salute you.'

Nwabuno walked further along
And her gaze fell on Akunne
A shifty looking fellow.
It was not going to be a kind exchange.

'The wooden gong does not call a short man for nothing,'
Nwabuno said. Akunne replied, conciliatorily,
'Ya, but the hand tells the wooden gong what to say.'
Nwabuno, mellowing off, then said,
'Akunne, son of Umueze,[16]

Diminutive and powerful, I salute you.
A wealthy man eats palm kernel in the bush,
It is an admissible conduct.
But when a poor man does the same,
He is chided for discourteousness.
A talk is not often as big as its talker.
Yet, you who were known to pursue a tortoise
So furiously, tell us if it was known to fly.

'Oliliuwa, the chicken thief of Ebonano,[17]
I salute you.
'A meal fills only the stomach of the meal eater,'
You were fond of saying.
But when the mouth is found guilty,
The jaws sit as if they are at a funeral.
An adult who breaks a pottery,
Often blames the pottery's age.
We all knew of your stock in trade.
Who else, but you, would insist
That a chicken bites when asked
To fetch the sacrificial rooster.
When he who is being treated of elephantiasis
Develops a running stomach,
We must first inquire if he left
Anything in the evil forest.
Oliliuwa,[18] I salute you.

'Nwankwo Ezimo, son of Uruokpalabani,[19]
A busy machete that never rusts – that is you.
You who is called the ant, I salute you.
You always had a reason to be busy
Who should blame you?
We all do, because
You chanced upon an elephant's carcass,
But were still digging for crickets.
Nwankwo, let the miser visualize
The look of the dead man's mouth.
About your compulsive habits, you would submit

That a chicken makes its droppings mindlessly
And effortlessly because it is killed in like manner.
Then you would claim that a dog does not sleep,
When there is meat on the grill.

'Nwankwo, was it not for men like you
That we urged busy farmers to make occasional trips
To their mother's relatives, for when it comes
Time to flee, the yam barn would not be a hiding place.
Nwankwo Ezimo, I salute you.

'Nwokeocha of the tattered tenement,
Son of Uruezenebo,[20] I salute you.
Your radical views intrigued us so.
Beyond food, you said there were
Three things that men needed most:
Heroes, myth and sex,
And palm wine, a distant last.

'I salute your candor on the day
Of the great debate with Nwoye,[21]
For Nwoye rose up and countered
That there were three things
That men needed most:
Palm wine, palm wine and palm wine.
Nwoye, history has never known
A libertine of your ilk.'

'Shut up, flippant imbecile,'
Nwoye yelled from the crowd,
His barrel voice drowning out the din.
'Palm wine unlocks tongues, unbinds souls,
Disperses thoughts and enhances
The tribology of friendship.
What more could a man desire?
Nwabuno, you are simply a fowl
That could never learn toilet manners.'

Ignoring Nwoye, she continued,
'There were men whose acts of stupidity
Baffled us. First, there was Asiegbunam
Son of the medicine man from Umuanua[22]
Who set out to count all the permutations
Of his own voice and lost his mind.

'Then there were the five foolish men
Of Uruoboa,[23] who matched skills
At hair splitting contest
Until they lost their minds and
Hunger crept into their households.
But even then, none of these
Were more striking than you
Odikaibe, you of the rotten dentition.

'Odikaibe, son of Umudu,[24]
We sometimes mourn a well-aged life,
Not because of its death
But because it never began.
I remember you
On the waning days of your sanity.
First, you ceased to be charitable with greetings
For you were always heard murmuring,
'Greetings are a chore.
A mouth may respond to greetings,
But the heart knows its enemies.'

'Under the oil bean tree,
At the gathering ground of Egwe-egwe,[25]
You would ask in great perplexity,
'Does a blind man's stick reinvent light?
Can anyone qualify his anxiety for
A shaft of light?' You paused
And one could answer. Then you asked,
'How great is the leisure of a solitary insect
Flying around the oil lamp?
How serene is the goat eating its curd

Under the shade, at the fallow grounds
Of Owa?' You paused and no one could answer.
Then you asked, 'Does a cattle have friends
In a good grazing ground?
Do animals dream?
Can they be trans-substantiated?
Does there habit within them,
The emotions of anger, fear, and jealousy
Which are the very outbacks of spirituality?'

'Then you asked, 'Do the stars smile or frown?
Are they intent on harm or good?'
Again, there was a long and futile pause.
Who knew Odikaibe, men's minds must float
Sometimes for knowledge weighs heavier
Than a tree trunk and wearies all who acquire it.

When you finally became a lunatic
Of the market place, we asked why
Your verbalizations were an endless
String of questions. At which you said,
'He who knows all has not asked
All the questions.' Then we knew that
Your ambition was to know all
By asking all the questions and not
By knowing all the answers.
Odikaibe, only a fool courts excessive knowledge.
I salute you.

'Adimora,[26] great son of Uruonyejem,[27]
Tell me more about causes and effects,
Of reasons and *adreasons*.
Polemicists that fell tragic
Upon his deep analytical insights.
Your brain was a swamp
That only the gods could drain.
Adimora, I salute you. I remember your
Favorite saying whenever Nwoye engaged you.

'A stupid argument is a bad weed
That must be nipped in the bud,' you would say.
If Nwoye pressed you further, you would say,
'Only a fool argues with a fool.'[28]
And then you would walk off to let the drunk
Contemplate the smell of his bad breath.
You cautioned the sons of Uruonyejem
To cultivate kindness like yam
Because even a wicked man appreciates kindness.
Adimora, I salute you.

'Ekemezie's wife,[29] daughter of Urumegwalu,
I salute you.
The early riser cooks with a bad knife.
Was there any but you who would
Not appreciate a beautiful ornament?
Your husband was of exemplary kindness,
Yet you always had a reason to be bitter.
True, when an animal is slaughtered
That women may not eat,
There should be a sudden absence of salt and spices,
True, an old woman may curse when she stumbles,
But swearing was your preoccupation.
Was it not death that said to the irascible
Old woman, the angry soul,
You and I are like the dung to the dung beetle?
Ekemezie's wife, you cried death more
Often than the orphan cries food
And made shallow the passions of death.
We are surprised you lived till you died.
Ekemezie's wife, I salute you.'

Ekemezie's wife would not take it.
She lounged towards Nwabuno,
But was held back. She said angrily,
'I salute you back,
If that is the edge you seek from
Your stupid greetings.

An old woman who is often reminded
To wipe her face asks if anyone
Was interested in eating her head upon her death.
Nwabuno, who would blame you.
The cockroach is a town crier in a homestead without hens.'

Nwabuno ignored her, and continued,
'Ezenwanmadu,[30] son of Ezira, first son of Nimo,
Redoubtable doyen of medicine men, I salute you.
Your personality and Nwoye's
Are as incongruous as can be,
Yet you both share an abiding friendship.
Ezenwanmadu, I salute you.

'Akukalianze, son of Abba, I salute you.
As a young man, you boasted about
The size of your endowment.
It is true that the long-horned cattle
Does not complain of headaches,
But what good was your endowment when
All you made were girls by all three of your wives?
When you instructed your wives to visit Izaka, we warned you
That a fertile land is not always too far from home,
That a man does not eat with another's mouth,
That a hawk and a fowl do not feed from the same dish.

'Indeed, a man who befriends Izaka is like a goat
Which belongs to a very sick man.
If he recovers, there is a feast, and the goat dies
If he dies, there is a funeral, and the goat dies
Either way, the goat dies.
And so it happened that all the boys
Izaka sired for you were useless,
And were all killed when they turned to thievery
As their stock in trade.
Akukalianze, we warned you that children are like salt
It is not always he who has more salt that has more salt.
Akukalianze, I salute you.

'Ezeako, son of Ebonato, grand son of Nwawelugo,
Most affable of men, I salute you.
Men are men's guardians.
He who has men, has wealth and admiration.
Thus, your ways were genuinely modest.
Yet, in spite of your good nature
You never got married.
We might ask you, 'the bachelor
Who eats his yam off the fireplace,
Is he not trying to avoid sharing it?
The groans of a bachelor while putting
Out a fire, is it not a sure indication
That he needs a woman?
Ezeako, I salute you.

'Ezedumeme, the reclusive one,
First son of Ezenwanmadu, I salute you.
You had the composure
Of a sputtering soup pot,
The temperament of a desert snake,
And the aloofness of an aging monkey,
Leader of the harem.
You dissembled not.
You preferred that your works, not you, may define you.
You insisted that no man's accomplishments
Was beyond the reach of his fellows.
For a man done growing, waits for others.
Honest one of the fewest words, I salute you.

'Udemezue,[31] son of Okeke Anichie
Son of Uruzu, I salute you.
There is but one apprehended reality
And you know it,
That we are all surreal patchworks
In the consciousness of God
And all toil is vain,
The toils of hate and love
In God's dream head

And when he awakes
He will make mythic stories of us
At heaven's play ground, and dream again.

'Okeke,[32]son of Agidi, son of Ajanzo
Vagrant tradesman, I salute you.
You announced your dreams at every stop, so be it.
But he who swears by what he dreamt,
Let him announce who dreamt with him.

'Ezeudo, son of Umudunu, of the rainmakers' clan,
I salute you.
The storm was over, but
We had not seen the sunny rays.
What we heard were distant claps
Of thunder returning to their storehouses
We had not seen the sunny rays.
Ezeudo, I salute you.

'When we cast our eyes
In the direction of Abacha,[33]
We heard the rumbling in the majestic skies
We knew, you Amaechi, last son of Oyeocha,
Son of Uruchime,
You also of the rainmakers' clan
Were up to your evil ways.
Amaechi, I salute you, but
Where should we have sought shelter
From that impending storm
Whose winds were howling in the forest of Abacha?

'Nwoye Akubue,[34] son of Ezira,
You and your caste of interpreters,
I salute you as well.
A fool does not realize that his brother is a guest.
An idle man is known by the way he ties his loincloth.
Nwoye, you busted all the bounds of etiquette.
A beggar does not ask for multiple favors at once,

But never you, Nwoye of the palmwine breath.
At harvest time, you go from *obi* to *obi*,[35]
Announcing your merry presence with the famous words,
'Celebrate life, celebrate life to the fullest.
Poverty is the only thing whose seasonal death
We are compelled to celebrate.'
Nwoye, how quickly you forgot that
An invitation to eat was not an invitation to drink.
Your stomach was likened to that of the land -
Both never got filled.

'During the dry season,
You were often heard preaching,
'Let he who has palm fruit give to the grass cutter
For the latter does not climb.'
Nwoye,[36] when was your height an incapacitation?
Was it not for you that it was often said,
'Those who grow beard like Nwoye,
Have others who squat before their tripods
To clear their ashes and light their fire.'

'Nwoye of the merry man's paradox,
I salute you.
You who is freer than all free men
But whose brilliant mind is caged
In kegs of palm wine, I salute you.

'We remember you on the days of abstract
Inquisition, on the feast of cocoyams,
At the gathering grounds of Egwe-egwe,
Where you stood tallest, for when asked
What love was, you said, 'Love is a strange,
Powerful, nondescript feeling of extremely
Benevolent regards for another or thing
So much so that the self is both
Willingly jeopardized and freely yielded.'

'Nwoye, we know you were not man enough to marry
Your thesis irks me like the vain articulation
Of a mighty hypocrite.'[37]

'*Tufia*, impudent bastard,'
Someone swore in the background.
It was Nwoye.

Ignoring him, Nwabuno went on,
'On that same day after
You had drunk your full, we asked
What time was, and you said,
'Time is a concomitant to the notion
Of reality; being the medium of propagation
Of all that is conscionable in thought
Or form; there being two fundamental dimensions,
Time and truth, a combination of which yields
The third, existence, all of them being mere notions.'

'Nwoye of the merry man's paradox,
If I did not know you, I would
Have thought that your addiction
To palm wine was a mere notion.'

'Shut up, Nwabuno,' Nwoye yelled.
Obviously riled. 'Can a brilliant thought
Hatch without the aid of that glorious drink?'

Ignoring him, Nwabuno went on,
'Nwagu,[38] the lecher of Uruokofia,[39] I salute you.
A fool is known by his assignations.
When we saw your rotten teeth,
We knew you had made another successful
One of those. I salute you and the spirit
That upheld your egregious appetite.
On certain days, we remember your
Immortal words for you said that
A wife's rabid mood called for the

Escalation of sexual activities,
But men were too foolish to oblige.
'A cow,' you said, 'does not appreciate its tail until it is cut off.'
'Who would not want to be the bag
That a maiden carries,' you were fond of saying.

'Eloka,[40] adulterous wife of Akaji,
Daughter of Umudiaba, I salute you.
The adulterous wife says that a headful of firewood
Is the best alibi.
It is true that the hand that holds a woman
Is not always her husband's
And that a beautiful and unfaithful wife
Is not punished by divorce, she soon marries.
But let the adulterous wife who says
Her husband is terrible realize that abused women
Have no mouth to talk.'

'The poor man complains incessantly
About the conduct of his wife.
Is there anyone who does not know
That a goat that is fed by two people dies of hunger[41]'
Eloka's mother came to her defense.

Akaji's mother said,
'An overfed woman uses her legs
To pack firewood under the tripod.
It is with great reluctance that a good adult
Lay hands on a child.
Yet, the child who requests for chewing stick
Before he has grown any teeth,
May be treated like an adult.'

'Ya,' Eloka's mother replied,
'The rat that outruns a child
Is accused of a deadly odor.'[42]

It took one look from the elders to remind
These women that Nwabuno was still speaking.
Who turning sideways addressed
Ekwutosi, barren wife of Enweani, daughter of Otenyi.

'Wipe your tears, O paragon of beauty,
Let time judge the days of our lives.
For God's gift they are, children of the world.
Through you, flesh and blood
And through God, vastly different entities.'

Drumbeat! Drumbeat!

Ekwutosi sobbed!
'*Ewuu Chimu!*' Ekwutosi's heart break was palpable.

'*Did we make the good palm oil?*
Was it not made by the good palm fruit?
Was the good palm fruit
Not made by the good palm tree?
Was the good palm tree
Not made by the good God?'

The drum died as abruptly
As it began, and Nwabuno continued:

'Ekwutosi, salt of salts,
Gentle dog raised by an old woman,
Tender voice that soothes the pain of angry words,
Beauty's ornament,
Beauty of the whole tribe,
What happened to your beauty?
Were you mocked because you were barren?
Was that why you dried up like
The severed stem of a creeping plant?'

Ekwutosi was sobbing audibly.
'Ekwutosi, please hold your tears.

Of all kind women,
You were most deserving of children.
But it is still an inexplicable fact of life,
That the pumpkin does not grow for the vegetarian
That the breadfruit falls
For those who have no teeth.

'Wipe your tears, Ekwutosi, tender one,
It is not those who have the best teeth
That smile the best. Besides
Those who do not have children, do not
Worry about the heart- rending act of
Child burial. For who can forget
The anguish of Okwuaku, wife of Ezenta, son of Uruchime,
When she lost her second and last son?'

Drumbeat! Drumbeat!

'When cocoyam begins to look impressive
People tend to forget it was a woman's handiwork.
'Mgboye, wife of Odike, son of Uruanyiugani,
Widowed at an early age, I salute you.
We know how hard you worked.
Harder than Nwoye Akubue of the palm wine breath,
And harder than the shameless titled men
Who spent all their time going from
One funeral ceremony to another,
And the rest of what was left,
Carving out elaborate rituals
Making it harder for others
To join their ranks.'

At this, there was a grumbling among
The titled men, who were distinguishable
From their goat skin garbs,
Knives held waist high. Some spat
In disgust. Others smiled wryly
In embarrassment. It was obvious that

Nwabuno was not the suavest of spokespersons.
An elder was heard saying:

'The overzealous dancer who points to the ground...
Is the latter made of her mother's skin?'

The drummer came to the rescue
Infusing a bit of humor.

'A rude speech demands an equally rude response,
But a wiry person is uneasy when proverbs
Are made of bones.'

Drumbeat! Drumbeat!

Then turning towards a group of
Bare breasted girls, Nwabuno said,
'A ripe corn is felt with the eyes.
Behold her beauty,
With rapturous joy, proclaim Nwakaego![43]
Tell of her beauty at Abagana, at Abba, at Ezi Owelle,
Proclaim her beauty in all the gathering places of Umu Owelle
Announce her beauty at Agu Ukwu
At Enugwu Ukwu, at Abacha, at Oraukwu,
And lands far flung from Ezira, Nimo.
Let the broad-chested bachelors of Ogidi
Vie for the honor to buy her yam tubers,
And the craftsmen of Igboukwu
Make ornaments celebrating her beauty,
And the loud-mouthed men of Ogbunike
Stay home with their dwarf he-goats.

'Nwakego, the trading caravans of Aro chukwu
Have spread your fame throughout Igbo land.
The goat rearers of Mbaise, the hunter-warriors of Ohaofia,
The cloth makers of Uturu, the great fishermen of Asaba,
The yam farmers of Ntezi, the renowned wrestlers of Nsukka,
The boat makers of Ikwere, the barn makers of Afikpo,

Even Adamu, the king of Igala and Ekete,
The mighty prince of Edo
Fantasize about your beauty.

''Behold,' they all say, 'the young maidens of Nimo
Silent joy. Cause of many
Extemporaneous celebrations,
Potentiated by the power of beauty
And by same, enchanter, evoker of dreams.'

'Behold her of Nimo,
Full of brilliance and glitter,
And her physical constitution,
Radiant, rounded and all,
And her skin, smooth as silk,
Firm as a ripe mango fruit,
And soft as a goose feather,
And the carriage that flows
Into her waist,
Evocatively garbed in beads.

'Behold her refulgent countenance,
And her eyes,
Choreographic stage of the sun's rays,
And her dimpled smile,
Evincing of the artistic touch of body molders.

'Behold her wholesome beauty
Of glistening ebony,
That cannot be peeled,
Ripened of the brash of adolescence,
Solid as pure gold, daring the elements.
Can she of the adolescent beauty
Urge beauty upon another?
See her, just turning puberty's corner,
See her, efflorescence branch,
Oblivious of the harsh realities of life.

'Behold her, and how they were smitten
Men, such as, who caught a glimpse of her.
And Izaka, that slave to passion,
Who when confronted said,
'A virgin's beauty is drool-worthy
And to spill me between her moist cleavage
Is gloriousness itself.
Hence, I desire the choicest maiden
In all the earth, wherefore,
I chose the people of Nimo.''

At this point, a profoundly uneasy
Silence fell on the assembly.
The drumbeat died to a solemn,
Somewhat subdued tone.
A mist fell on the assembly
And murkily visible, embedded in the mist
Removed ways from the gathering,
Was an immense presence that smirked
Of power and menace.
It was surpassing in ugliness.
A lone barking dog was hushed.
Children rushed to the safety
Of their mother's laps and the men
Queasily held onto their knives.
And the drummer resumed his
Unrelenting strokes.

'*The big tuber that trembles*
Never reaches a strange land.'

Drumbeat! Drumbeat!

'The things that fear,' I muttered,
'Stumble before me who dwells
In the presence of the God of Jacob.
Because he is with me, I stand a majority,
In the company of my God,
No evil shall I fear.'

Endnotes

[1] Although there was a dimensional confluence of sorts, I was out of my element and it took Okonkwo's glance to remind me that I was only meant to be a passive observer.

[2] Nimo is comprised of twenty seven precincts.

[3] A precinct of Nimo.

[4] Vegetarian and Poet.

[5] A precinct of Nimo.

[6] A precinct of Nimo.

[7] It was said that Obidigbo never knew how to pursue women and always waited for his brothers to get married, and thereafter killed them to   possess their wives.

[8] Flutist and medicine man. He was never seen without his flutes.

[9] Precint of Nimo. Home to many legendary warriors of old and men such as Nwoye and Ezenwammadu who were renowed for their great intellect.

[10] Uvoko's wife.

[11] Was responsible for manhood initiation rituals.

[12] A precinct of Nimo.

[13] Pestles are used to mash boiled yams or cassavas in mortars. In a densely cluttered neighborhood during lunch or dinner time, the sound of pestles going off at various mortars actually produced music that brought joy to the minds of hungry men who were looking forward to gulping down long juicy strands of bitter leaf soup with their mashed yam or cassava.

[14] Titled woman. Talkative.

[15] Never married. Generally kept to himself.

[16] A precinct of Nimo.

[17] A precinct of Nimo.

[18] No one is sure how Oliliuwa died: Whether as a result of diarrhea or due to his elephantiasis or both.

[19] A precinct of Nimo.

[20] A precinct of Nimo.

[21] Ex-husband of Nwabuno. Philosopher and friend of Ezenwanmadu.

22 A precinct of Nimo.

23 A precinct of Nimo.

24 A precinct of Nimo

25 An assembly ground, roughly in the center of Nimo.

26 Metaphysicist.

27 A precinct of Nimo.

28 Adimora really resented Nwoye whose argumentation tended to be   convoluted unlike Adimora who was more opinionated and conclusory in the way he examined his universe.

29 Had an annoying habit of cooking in the wee hours of the morning. The sound of her pestle while mashing her condiments woke everybody up.

30 His great healing craft nurtured Izaka to health.

31 He insisted that everything was a mere illusion.

32 Confidence man. Claims his dreams foretell the future.

33 A nearby town to Nimo.

34 Nwoye's father was Akubue. Nwoye was extremely good at interpreting palm wine.

35 The homestead of a wealthy man.

36 Nwoye was close to seven feet tall and lazy and was fond of saying that he who carries nothing, breaks nothing.

37 Nwabuno has never seized to blame Nwoye for their divorce. And yet you could sense that she has never ceased to be drawn to Nwoye's prodigious intellect.

38 Highly sought after by barren women. Always boasted about how he could make any woman happy.

39 A precinct of Nimo.

40 Eloka had five children, only the first was by her husband, who often beat her. Her waywardness brought her great derision

41 In fact, Akaji's mother was the main provider for the household and she resented her daughter-in-law's wayward manners.

42 Claiming that Akaji's poverty was the reason why her daughter became wayward.

43 Literally means "a child is better than wealth."

Chapter 14

Song of Izaka

O death, O tyrannical one,
How cruel the means by which you attain
Your necessary ends.
For without you, no birth can be justified.
Would that you were neither ugly nor arbitrary,
Would that you were not cruelly kind,
Would rites, spring, of renewal not
Be properly presaged?
O death, you have no handsome face.

Nwabuno stepped cautiously forward,
Facing the misty presence,
Adjusting her loin cloth, squaring up,
Mustering up vigor; defiant
In gait and words, muttering to herself...
Finally said she to the relief of all:

'Here is the story of Izaka,
Half man, half god, spirit of the rain forest,
Patron of proliferators, maker of civilizations,
Addler, pace setter and standard bearer
For practices that could imperil the inquirer.

'Here is Izaka that must be accepted.
Inquire not.

'Here is Izaka,
A hunter of men,
A warden of evil,
A protector of women,
An irreproachable predator.

'Here is Izaka,
Capricious as the desert sand,
Who runs when he says we should walk,
Who walks when he says we should run.

'Here is Izaka that must be hailed,
Hail Izaka! Warden of passion,
From him no man is safe,
But all women are loved.

'This is Izaka,
This is he of equestrian ardor,
This is he of whom Agubanze the poet says,
'All glory, glory loud
All honor, round and round.'

'Hail Izaka!
Bough of the Iroko tree,
The biggest bough in the rain forest,
The bough that burdens
The tree that bears it,
The tree on top a tree,
The great tree that defies
The climbing rope.

'Hail Izaka!
The great tree that is known by its roots,
The root that traverses the trudging path,
And all human traffic detour from it,
The nut that defies the cracking stone,
The tendinous meat that fatigues an earnest jaw,
The fire that burns without faggots,
The wild fire that scorches the sea soken weed,
The shouter whose voice
Breaks the silence of a dark and gloomy night.

'Izaka, the strong man with the biggest rump,
When he turns his back to you …
He beclouds your vision.

'Izaka, he who masturbates at dusk
Before the setting sun,
In full view of the children of the valley.
How rebarbative, that singular conduct.

'Izaka of perpetual youth,
The breeding stallion,
The farm's mainstay,
The provider of food and fun,
Who canters about with vim and pride,
Consummating the breeding force
That burns within him
Like an unleashable inferno.
Taking pleasures from here and there,

He has never been bridled,
Never been mounted, he does
All the mounting in town.
He makes thoroughbreds
But is not of their stock.
He is so pleased with himself
He says he is simply glorious.

'Izaka, you are the wild beast
Whom we approached with our best arrows,
When you turned and looked at us,
We quivered and sought your appeasement.

'You are the great beast,
You sleep wherever you please.
You are the sacred python,
You sleep whenever you want.
You are the elephant,
You roam at the hunter's backyard.
Often did we conspire to hunt you
Yet face to face, we were awed
And we turned back in shame.
Izaka, you are beyond us.

'You are the impulsive slayer of men.
And your bestiality astounds us.
Whatever killed the lion is
Greater than the lion - by which
We mean you and death.
Izaka, you terrify us.

'Izaka, the swamps are set ablaze
When you sneeze; your immense nostrils,
They truly terrify us.

'Indeed, Izaka, you are everything
And everything is you.
Everything, that is, that is despicable.

You are the angelic villain,
The ascetic hedonist,
The foul-mouthed stooge
Of the rain forest,
The authoritarian conqueror of widows,[1]
And when it pleases you,
You snatch a man's wife
Before her husband's petrified face.

'Izaka, like a good poet
You have a thousand personalities,
And each is the most outstanding we know.

'Izaka, you are a bogey,
Our infants hold their tears
When we say, 'Here is Izaka.'
We fear what you might do next.
You conquer your enemies in the day,
At night, you console them.
You are a stalwart for the poor,
But when it pleases you,
You stomp away on them.

'Izaka, never was there a story teller
Who could narrate all that you did or said.
Izaka, we fear what you might do next.

'Your speeches glowed like the morning sun,
Yet were full of sand.
You exhorted us to moral uprightness
And you over topped it with obscene expletives.
Izaka, we fear what you might do next.

'Izaka, you were the Machiavellian
Ruler of our villages and towns,
Yet there was no threat to your hegemony.
We do not love you, we do despise you,
Yet we cannot imagine life without you.

We will always fear you.
You who swings death's scythe
In such wide perilous swoops.

'Izaka, are you not the despot
Who is not subject to the rules
By which he imposes upon his people?
Izaka, you are simply beyond us.

'Who compares with you
And falls not short?
We cannot compare in good works
Nor in bad works
Nor in works which defy a string of words.
Even Ezenwanmadu, chief among
The interpreters matched wits with you
Much to his ignominy.

'The elders say of the wild
Ever nodding lizard,
'Here is an animal, here is he
Of whom everything has a rationale merit,
Here is he who nods for Izaka
In constant admiration and sometimes
Scuttles in anticipative excitement.'

'Izaka, did you not say of the lizard,
'Here is he, here is a friend indeed
Here is he, the understander, the appraiser,
He appraises me to my excellent delight.'
Izaka, we fear what levels
Of absurdities you can sink to.

'Glorious deeds are sung of you
By the outcoming maidens,
And your valor is known throughout the land.
The young acolytes and initiates to manhood
Are taught that you are the villainous character

Who takes a man's life when it is sweetest to him.
For was it not you who said,
'When your moans reach a deafening crescendo,
When your gyrations reach the climatic
Act of harmony, play guard.
When you contort your face,
Disavowing the moistness
That gives you pleasure, play guard.
When you break abruptly,
Precipitating your soul, play guard.
When you momentarily swirl out of your body
And into it again, play guard.
When you heave that sigh of joy
And prepare to savor to the fullest
That great mimicry of death, play guard.
I take a man's life when it is sweetest to him.'
Izaka, what obscenities.

'Still, Izaka, our maidens sing of your valor
They say, 'May my husband's stamina be like
That of Izaka.'

'The old men of the village speak with pride
About their encounters with you,
And swap of you, their fondest memories
With tapsters, assiduous of palm wine,
Who likewise command attention
By their nocturnal contacts with you.

'Izaka, when asked about your pride, you said,
'Pride breeds prudery, breed arrogance,
Breeds imposture, breeds false ethics,
Pride puts on a false garb on the naked ape.
Do you say I'm proud when I parade undressed,
And let you see my patch of silken grass,
And you behold my tree trunk in its full arousal,
As I dangle my humility before the world?'

'Izaka, we fear what you might say next.

'Izaka, you do have the credibility of
A rabid preacher, which is none at all,
And you impress us as much as a
Conservative Westerner, who insists that
There is virtue in bigotry,
And rulership by the wealthy is only
Pragmatic to be maintained,
And all else is communism or liberalism
To be thoroughly despised,
And to imagine the world in dialogue
Is naivete to be avoided;
Politics after all being the game of princes,
With power belonging to the shrewd and astute,
Most certainly to the ruthless and uncompassionate.

'Izaka, did we not call you a tyrant
Without alliances and you said,
'Whose good works compare with mine?'
We reminded you that a tyrant sometimes
Unwittingly does good works and you said,
'Are my wits not deeply embedded in me?
Am I not always wrapped up about my wits?
Not like a fern shallowly anchored to the
Armpits of a palm tree, not like a climbing
Plant desperately clinging to its host,
No, not like one of those. Are my wits
Not deeply rooted in me?'

'Izaka, we know you are a wordsmith
And we have heard your poems
Rendered by the parrots, and the owls
Who hoot in reluctant accompaniment.
It is foolhardy to try to lay guilt on you.

'Izaka, never was there a story teller
Who could narrate all that you did or said.

We fear what you might say next.

'When Oliobu, the greatest wrestler who ever lived,
When Oliobu of the legendary upper body strength
Whose shoulders were said to be made of iron
Forged by Chiuzu[2] himself,
When Oliobu, whose thighs were like
The mounds of glistening red earth
Upon which we planted yam, cocoyam, corn,
Melon and okra, when Oliobu, whose calves were
Like yam tubers harvested from the fertile
Swamps of Otuamu, when Oliobu,
Whose blood vessels were like the wild running
Roots of the fibrous cocoyam,
When Oliobu girded his loincloth
And gestured in challenge towards you,
You cracked his shoulders in five places,
Each to a cattle that must be rendered
In appeasement.

'Izaka, was there ever a barren woman
That was brought to your chambers,
Whose stomach did not swell with pride?
Was it not you, Izaka, who killed
Ekwutosi, the barren wife of Enweani
Who had sought fertility herbs
From the best medicine men of Abacha
Of Abagana, of Agulu, of Agu ukwu,
And ignored all the pleas to visit your chambers
For she insisted that a woman may not
Knowingly beget the devil's child.

'Izaka, you are the ox
Whose bastards are called princes of the valley.
The very fair maidens of Urukweluora,[3]
Fairer than any maidens known on earth,
More beautiful than the mermaids of Otuamu,
And fair indeed, for they were the pride

Of Umuigbo, were called Umuizaka ‑
The daughters of Izaka.

'Izaka, you are not the only lecher we know
When Otuba,[4] son of Otiaba,
Who lost his index finger to whitlow
Killed his wife and slept with his daughter,
You strangled him.
Izaka, if it was customary to kill the incestuous man,
It would be right to first kill the randy he-goat.
Although some say, Otuba's wife was your lover,
We believe it was right for Otuba's energies to die.
But Izaka, who frowned before your own excesses.

'When Egwuatu, the medicine man from Umueze,
Reputed for his long and tedious incantations,
Confronted you, he became an ordinary mad man
And paraded the streets of the market place,
And died ignominiously on the wedding day of his
Daughter, Egoka. Soggy and drunk, he drowned
In the drinking well[5] that his forearms had dug.
Izaka, we fear what you might do next.

'When we reminded you that
You had stepped on Izakaocha, son of Afuluenu,
Daughter of Mgbajiukwu, one of your numerous bastards
And lunatic of the market place, you said,
'Only a fool memorizes the configuration of faces,
Only a weakling keeps count of his sleeping partners,
To remember my children is to impute weakness to me.
I have sired both trees and men.
Only I knows where the face of a tree is hidden,
And where her genitals are embedded.
Besides, when a woman is pregnanted standing up,
She necessarily gives birth to a mad child.
I have spoken.'

'Indeed, Izaka, you have spoken.

'When you struck Nwankwo Otiegwu,
The flute musician of Ebonato,
We charged you with murder,
But you said, 'A bad music is a constant
Assault on the mind.
Just like the blood of a gaunt offering
Sullies the sacrificial table,
So does a bad music, the mind.
Like the assault of overseasoned food on the palate,
Like the assault on the mind of Nwokolo,
The boastful farmer of Uruezebaluchi,[6]
When the gods rained recalcitrant weeds
On his farm. O it irks me, like the smile
On the face of the fat, fatuous and
Ugly Mgbafor of Atukpolom
When she pleaded my indulgence,
After she had on three previous occasions,
By inadvertence or sheer neglect,
Slept on the children of her womb
Whom I had made for her.'

'Still, Izaka, the deaths of Nwankwo
And Mgbafor are hardly justified.
You are simply beyond us.
We suppose you have spoken.

'Izaka, was it not you who destroyed
Nwafor Omenka, son of Ogbulie of Amafum,
The most celebrated craftsman in all the land,
Because he did not erect a bold and handsome
Statue to you. Omenka erected a statue to Ani,
Of the universe, a god, and it was appropriate
That it arched into the belly of the sun.
But of you and your numerous bastards,
Of you who beguiled our maidens,
We saw it worthy not to honor your evil ways.

'You would later boast that he who ate you
And ate palm nuts knows which is the jawbreaker.
Izaka, you are terrible,
You must be appeased.

When you thrashed about in orgasmic convulsions,
The forest shook.
Once Ibezim, the garrulous tapster of Awato[7]
Fell off the palm tree, you throttled him.
He had seen you when your life was sweetest to you.
We had warned Ibezim
Not to visit the palm clusters
At the outlet of Ojita at odd times.
Or perhaps did you throttle him
Because he had seen you with Ugoye
One of the numerous wives of Eze Onyiaobodo?[8]

'Ugoye was gentle, corpulent and voluptuous
And her big breasts caught the whim of the King.
Ugoye was reputed for the taste of her melon soup
And the skill with which
She justified it with pounded yam.
But she was relegated among the King's wives
Because her big breasts could not suckle a
Male child with a big head.

'Izaka, this was on the day of the big tragedy
That struck on the big market day,
The day that the sacred tree, Ukpakaegbutunma,[9]
Fell and the birds dispersed.

'When a stranger's corpse is being carried
It is as if one is carrying a log of wood.
For on that same day, Ezedumeme,
First son of Ezenwanmadu, fast, furious,
Temperamental, successful beyond
Any members of his age group,
Always running, trotting only when at rest,

And never stooping to frivolous traditions,
Said that you, Izaka, were a capricious outcast
From the family of gods,
And that your stubby fingers
Would not let you enjoy okra soup,
You struck him on both legs
And forever he lost their use.

'Izaka, if you are not vagarious,
How else can we understand you?
Ezedumueme never attended any functions
To your honor, for he insisted that he would
Not laugh with a king, unless he would also
Share his regalia.

'Izaka, was it not you that ruined Ibueze
The wealthiest farmer in the village of Ebonano,[10]
Because he starved his first wife
In the midst of plenty?
Was it not for Ibueze that the people
Of Egbengwu were known as miserly,
Who preserve bananas in yam barns
Until they were too ripe for anyone to enjoy,
And sometimes washed their hands with saliva
Even in the midst of overflowing wells?

'Izaka, was it not you that stopped Ezeakor,
Of Ajanzo,[11] the bully, dead in his tracks
When he charged towards his mother
And saved Ifiteani[12] from the retribution of the gods.
Ikpeama, the great oral historian of Uruokokwe,[13]
Said you acted out of a penchant for justice
And Ezezue, the oral historian of Uruchime,[14]
Said Ezeakor's mother was your lover
And you acted out of a protective rage.
And I, Nwabuno, of the slippery tongue,
Of the village of Amafum,[15] said you, Izaka
Spared your lover and killed your own son.

'Izaka, your mysteries confound us so.
Even Ezenwanmadu of Ezira,[16]
The greatest medicine man of all
Twenty seven villages and beyond,
Who understood the language of spirits,
And interceded for people far and wide,
And was apt at wisdom better than
Anyone we have known, could not explain
Why you acted so.

'Ebenebe, the custodian of the rain forest
Was heard admonishing you that anger was a
Dangerous emotion that left victims long after its death.

'Izaka, so often did you hold
The specter of death before us,
But it was not until Nwanyiekie[17] died
That we knew you were as much affected by death as us.

'Yes, Izaka, you are the good poet
With a thousand personalities.
We have heard your songs
Rendered by the parrots,
And the owls who hooted in
Reluctant accompaniment.
We have even heard your songs
About the gentle evening breeze,
Whose deliberate presence was known
By the fluttering of the blades of the palm tree.
And the menacing harmattan breeze,
That howled in the forest
Heralding the big rain,
And of the golden sunset
Seen atop the trees
In the direction of Abacha,
And of your numerous songs of love
Celebrating the fulfillment of your chief mission,
But of all those songs, none

Touched our hearts like your lamentations
On the day Nwanyiekie died, belched out
In your deep guttural voice.

'We heard it, Izaka, when you cried,
'May the days at dawn never again
Embrace the retirement of dusk
And at dusk, may they never awaken
To the reinvigoration of dawn.
May the days at dawn not lose
The sheath that covers their nascency,
And at dusk, may they be frozen
With the wrinkles that announce their
Long and tedious journey.'

'Then Nwokolo, the town crier asked,
'Izaka, every butcher has a favorite knife,
But must fowls not come to roost?
Or farmers return from their farms?
Must men not embrace their wives tonight?
Must time in general cease to flow?'

'Ignoring him, Izaka cried,
'O fountain of treasure,
Inexhaustible, of constant cheer,
O vessel of honor and mystical joy,
O snug, strength's tower,
Amazing in might,
O queen of my soul, especially
In difficult times,
O beauty that no craftsman can capture,
O grace that no dreamer can conjure,
O Nwanyiekie, were that I were
Like you, a mere mortal, then would
I surely bow with you, in exit.

'What incomparable timber,
What dazzling polish,

That through her manners gleamed,
What charm for which no anger could not be doused;
She was full of goodness, was she,
And not a foible was felt,
But only by her grace matched,
That issued in endless driblets.

"How with the softness of an evening breeze
She whispered into my ears,
And melted into my feverish embraces.
And O most assuredly was she,
The shapeliest woman in all the lands,
And what pleasure, what currents of passion
Swept through my spine
When my tongue traced out the
Elaborate contours of her body,
Depositing a trail of saliva
Like a sentimental wildebeest.

"Then she reached down
And gently clasped my throbbing part,
Calmed and secured in her soft and balmy hands,
She guided me through the
Unfathomable abyss of pleasure
Expressly forbidden of the gods.
O how then, fusing contour to contour,
We locked up from morn till night,
Until amid sweat and abandon,
Our evolutionary best was declared,
And zest momentarily declined,
Then we parted briefly ever so,
Until the next welling of zest,
And we rose to fuse again
In pleasurable reunion.

"She was called the eagle's daughter,
Heiress of the avian world, and truly so
For she had the regality of a queen,

And the muted elegance of an egret,
And walked with the assurance of a secretary bird,
And each step she took,
Produced a titillating sway,
Captivating all who beheld it,
Whipping men into a swirling of sexual frenzy
Who claimed she was a theophany
Of the goddess of love.

''For indeed this was she of whom they said,
'Hark, fairer than the morning sun
Benign as the moon, and
Sparkling of character like
The early morning scoops of Ojita.''

'Then we said to Ebenebe,
Custodian of the rain forest,
'Organize a party of elders, to minister,
In commiseration with Izaka, let us go.'

'When at last Ebenebe declared,
'Death is unlike any journey:
There is no path by which men may return.
Izaka, our belabored hearts are
Sodden with sweat, the blurry eyes
Of our souls, they too are tear laden.

''Death is it, Izaka, is it,
Death is the impudent masquerade
That confronts the spirits,
That overcomes our saplings,
The equalizer, that confronts
The elders and the young,
The weak and the strong,
That is neither averse to night nor day,
That scoffs at the kind
And the wicked alike,
And at the diviner and his clients,

That is not impressed by beauty or ugliness,
That strikes the indolent and industrious,
That befalls the merrymaker
As surely as it does he who shuns him.
In its stealthiness, it creeps up to us
At a time when we are least willing to accept it.
Without so much as a greeting,
It proceeds to meticulously
Unravel all that we built,
And nullify our very existence.

"Death is it, Izaka, is it
That rivals you in whimsy,
That cannot be glamorized,
That must be embraced only
When he wills,
Whose purpose is known
Only to the council of gods
Who spawn intrigues,
And feed off the excitement
Of the drama we are forced to enact.

"We too mourn the death of Nwanyiekie.'

'In fury you drove us out,
Why fleeing we heard you say,
'Every man has two bags,
One for death and one for life.
With one he collects all
The indignities that set him apart,
And the other overturns it into
The uncaring turbulence of a stormy river.
Death is it that neutralizes the pride of life
And sends a man back by the lane
By which he came.

"O death, you consort not with time and space,
Nor with men erected in time and space

And substantiated with dirt.
Yet you are a rebel,
A mystical clearinghouse,
Arbitrary, inexorable, and clad with terror,
Even the gods are powerless before you.
Yet be not proud
For you are vulnerable to
Your own mighty hands.
For he who pins his opponent
To the ground is there bound.
And when you extinguish the
Flame of life, you also
Die of and in your self.

''The council of gods cannot decree my death,
I am more terrible than he,
I cannot be affected.
Not me, I say, not me,
Nor the eyes in me,
Nor the fabrics of my gut,
Nor the whisperer, the other me, living within,
Nor the lobes of my mind,
I cannot be affected, I,
Izaka, half man, half god,
Spirit of the rain forest,
Patron of proliferators,
Maker of civilizations,
I cannot be affected.'

'Izaka, we could have been deceived
Had we not seen the strain you bore.

'Izaka, at length have I spoken
But have only begun to scratch the surface.
Was there ever a story teller
Who could narrate all that you did or said?

'Izaka, was it not you who held up the sky
On the day the gods were intent on crushing us,
When Eze Onyiaobodo, alone, ate the sacrificial
Spoils of war and forgot to offer any to the gods of the land?

'Izaka, was it not you who walked
Ahead of the pall bearers
On the burial day of Itulu,
The terrible and feared medicine man of Obiagu Otenyi,[18]
And dispelled the evil spirits
Who were prowling for human sacrifices?
Those were valorous deeds indeed
For which you were known.

'Who was mightier than Izaka?
Mighty enough to wrestle
With Chianyanwu, the sun god.
Two full moons they wrestled,
Two full moons they rallied,
Back and forth they strained,
Forth and back, no one yielded,
Until Chiuzu, the patron of blacksmith
The god of fire, erected an iron curtain
Between the war farers
And Izaka took to the forest
And Chianyanwu took to the sky.

'Some historians say that
The mighty trees of the rain forest of Ojita
Are the upstanding hairs of Izaka
Propping the sun to the sky.

'O Izaka, knowledgeable in science
Better than any charlatan,
O Izaka, knowledgeable in mysteries
Better than any medicine man,
By your wisdom, you planted
Your hairs in the soil

So that they may forever sap
The strength of the sun god
Who promised to scorch to death
The great people of Nimo.

'Izaka of the thunderbolt's voice,
On the days you speak to us
Your voice rumbles like an impatient rain,
Rolling down the hillside,
Rushing to swell the swamps.
And when your voice thunders through the rain,
The elders say you are quarreling
With the sun god, for want of challenges,
You have carried your fight to the sky.

'Izaka, you are the rain
That the rainmaker foresees not.
And when you thunder away in anger,
The rainmaker's wife scurries for cover.

'In vain does the rainmaker
Try to dispel your thunderous rain.
For who is it that can gag your mouth?
When Oranmili, the rainmaker of Umueze[19]
Who had collected a fee from Ugonwa,
The widow of Nnabunie, son of Ezira, tried,
His hut was struck down,
His and his wive's also, and were swept away.
And in anger, you drenched the funeral party.
So badly did you soak the village of Umueze,
That it was wondered whether
Perhaps you had a problem with Nnabunie,
Or perhaps you desired Ugonwa,
The woman with the salty waist,
From whom you had requested favors
On the day she was bewailing her husband.
But you have been known to snatch
A man's wife from before her husband.

And so it was, that on the day
Of the big rain
The boastful rain makers
Carried their faces in shame.
For such was the nature of their trade.

'Izaka, it is not that we did not
Try to revolt against you.
For we remember on the second day
Of the festival of yams, when
Agubanze,[20] second son of Ezenwanmadu
Rose up with a mighty inspiration
At the gathering ground of Egwe-egwe
And said,

''Izaka looked at our eyes,
We backed down.
Izaka came close to us,
We stepped aside.
Izaka extended his hands,
We desired a hug.
Before he could speak,
We approved,
And deferred to his wisdom.
Without understanding what he had said,
We assured him that he was right.

''Then he smiled at us and it was
An occasion to laugh uproariously.
He held his gaze, we bashed.
We flung obsequity at him,
And generously threw compliments his way,
And glazed him with admiration,
And with affection out and out.

''Would any look at us and not see
The unhappy ghosts that dwell within,
The shackles that bind our minds.
Ours are wasted minds, and Izaka

Is the master that must be impressed.

''He had mentioned that the day was good
And we promptly concurred,
Suggesting that we would rejoice and be glad,
Adding that we were already
Overextended with joy, freedom and peace.

''People of Nimo, how can
Our shackled ghosts be free and at peace?
For we live in an opiated world of illusion,
Like solitary wayfarers we are,
The sole occupants of a long stretch of road
That our overwrought minds have carved.

''People of Nimo, we are structurally mad
But we are too afraid to tell ourselves.'

''O my God,' Agubanze continued,
'What terrible fate has befallen the sons of Ani.
We delight to do your will,
And your law is within our hearts.
But what is your own delight?
Surely, not that we men be free?
Or that peace may rest
Upon the poor man's mind?
How about redistributing justice,
So that no man may have
So much of one and none of the other?
Or would you brand us an evil race
Because we desire that no man
May live in fear of another?
And that all faces bear
A genuine and caring smile?

''Peace and justice are like two brothers,
One is older and overbearing.
The other is yielding, sometimes admiring,
But must be relegated.

''People of Nimo, we swallowed
The opium of the medicine man's peace
By redefining justice, misconstrued,
By making hallucinatory impositions,
We have let justice slip by us
And thus attained our kind of peace.

''Peace is that slave to justice
That constantly strokes his ego,
Urging it to remain kind and gentle.
Peace is that which belongs to the slave,
And justice to his master.
Peace is the nonviolent acquiescence
That the fiercer and oft violent
And oppressive justice urges on the oppressed,
So that the oppressor should exercise justice,
And the oppressed may uphold peace,
And no overlap may be allowed.

''People of Nimo,
Peace is not our lot.

''O my God, give us not peace.
Make us not savvy of the things
Philosophers dwell upon.
Make us not functional members
Of a dysfunctional society.
Give us not houses nor farms
Nor wives nor systemically degenerative jobs,
Nor any of the fruits which are considered
Just deserts of our acquiescence.
But first, set our society aright
And then give us our own just
Portion of redistributed justice.

''People of Nimo,
Our peace is a travesty.
For how can they have peace that die,
Or attain it, they that wallow in want?

For peace is that blankness
That characterizes the cessation of wants.
Being neither jealous, nor guarded, nor acquisitive,
Nor intrusive, nor externalizable, and being marked
By a profound feeling of rest, harmony, orderliness,
Mental stability, and calmness as of the dead,
And not being marked by the affected insouciance
Of a poor man's mind and especially
Of those who think that the bells of change
Toll not for them.

"O people of Nimo,
We do not have peace
Neither does he who have justice have freedom.
For just as they are not righteous,
Whom righteousness yawn, so are they
Not free whom freedom preach.
For those whose palm kernels were
Cracked by benevolent spirits,
Often think that palm kernels come with cracks.
And yet each, who with their conscience agree,
Legitimize their actions, and proclaim themselves
Owners of free wills and possessors of freedom,
Yet are unwitting actors of preassigned role
In the great drama of life.'

'Before Agubanze would finish,
The elders had slithered away.
On the day after he spoke,
We found him stricken and dead.
We asked Izaka, who said,
'When a child wrestles his father
To the ground, his father's testicles will
Cover his eyes. I have spoken.'
On the third Oye market day[21]
Following the death of Agubanze,
The elders made haste to see you.
There was Ezenwanmadu and Ebenebe
And Nwoye Akubue of the palm wine breath,

There were the elders of all
Twenty seven villages,
There was Okeke Ifezue, the blacksmith,
And Nwokolo, the farmer, and Nmouegbu,
The home builder, and Okonkwo, the drummer,
And Uvoko the flutist, and then there was I,
Nwabuno of the slippery tongue.

'Upon approaching the forest,
The elders said in unison,
'May the dog not bite the medicine man's bag,
May the medicine man not curse the dog.
May the ponds not dry up, may the fish not die.
May strength flow in their designated channels.
May the beasts fodder according to their designations.'

'Then we heard your reply from
The cover of the undergrowth, saying,
'Where mysteries lie, the prowler dares.
Are you driven by your philosophic instincts
Or shall you prey upon me?
Stalker of mysteries, how mysteries stalk you.'

'Then upon perceiving your apprehension,
Ezenwanmadu said, 'A servant does not show
His anger to the king. A child may not look
His father in the groin. But an irate servant
May cover his face with a basket and tell
The king off. Izaka, we have no basket.'

'Still not settled about our intentions,
Izaka asked, 'Who was that whose face we
Scratched in whom hatred was not stirred?
Who was that whom victim was
Whose vision was not skewed?
Who was that whose spine we twitched,
Who wriggled not like a hapless worm?
Who was that whose ego we smeared
Who did not slacken the belts of stoicism,

And sneeze in violent disgust of the gods?
May he who visits me not over stretch
The bounds of hospitality, and upon his departure
May his back not be hunched.

''Ezenwanmadu, can there be peace between men
And the gods who pelter their minds?
Still, let rodents fight the dog who spoils for a fight.'

'Then Ezenwanmadu spoke out saying,
'An errand is not delivered with proverbs.
Izaka, let palm oil not inundate
The words we eat. Like roast yam
Fit for a deserving farmer,
Let us scrape off the soot and dirt,
Let us sprinkle a proportionate measure of
Salt, spice and palm oil,
And let the beauty of words blossom,
To illumine the contents of our hearts
And let there be no flares or roaring.

''Peace, Izaka, peace, as only a man of peace could,
Peace as belongs to the care free and the innocent,
Peace as portrayed by the stolid chameleon,
And as enacted by the sloth, and by the animals
And plants in whose hearts there is no guile.'

'Then Izaka replied,
'Can they offer peace that die,
Or they that want,
When was peace their stronghold?
Even I, Izaka, does not have peace.
But speak in a manner presuming peace
So that my wrath may not overtake you
O medicine man.'

'Then Ezenwanmadu said,
With a hint of trepidation,
'Let me offer you then

The regularity and cadence
Of a well-practiced mind.
Let there be the nonidealized peace
As only a disciplined mind can offer
And let there be no flares or roaring.'

'Izaka, retorted, somewhat sharply,
'False peace is to the man
And discipline is to the fool in him.
There is error in conformity
And agony in privation.
I look at the trees and animals and
I do not see the discipline of which you speak
Surely O medicine man,
You speak to me as a fool would.'

'At which Ezenwanmadu said,
'A fool is sometimes led by instincts
Towards purposeful and directive behavior.
Say, let me speak as a fool would
But let me speak of truth instinctive,
Evident, de facto and,
Let there be no flares or roaring.'

'Then Izaka said,
'There is no such thing as truth or
Objective reality, without regard
To persons or circumstances.
A de facto truth is a circumstantial truth
That is necessarily false.
Truth as can be known by man
Is a consensus, borne out of a convenient
Frame of reference, about which he evaluates
The probability of untruth.

''Truth is inabsolute.
In your indeterministic world,
Truth can be circumstantial,

Experiential, utilitarian, personable,
And group oriented. And being highly
Manipulable, it can be untruthful.
Truth is a commuted reality, albeit highly mutable,
Being false, it becomes untruthful.
But those who have the greater consensus
Always beseem the greater truth.

'Speak then of the untruth which in
Your domain of reasoning and perception
Is most likely to be true, but forget
Not that our domains are not the same,
I being the wiser and more experienced.

'Prod O gently, the dry pod of wild peas
So that there be no flares or roaring
O medicine man.'

'Then Izaka threatened,
'Over the years, have men not been
Inspired by the logion of the medicine man?
Go, Ezenwanmadu, why must their source
Of inspiration dwindle?
Is a child sent to steal by his father
Not a bold thief?
If a dog is urged to run,
Would it not tend to overdo it?[22]
Men of Nimo, obviously,
You harbor resentment towards me.
Can smoke be buried?
Can a corpse be concealed from the ground?
Yet I dwelt in the forest
Not in your midst.
Is the respect due an idol
Not the two hands with which it was held?
I, being am, of the tribe of the gods,
Fully aware that the stone and the head
Cannot be playmates.

"Still excrement does not smell in the stomach.
Why then would Agubanze publicly assail me?
The smelling skunk raises questions
As to how much it intends to smell upon its death.[23]
People of Nimo, where is the respect
That is due an elder? Does a shouter
Shout his mother's name in the market place?
And yet do you not say that a child
Who makes proverbs with the finesse of his fathers
May be asked to repay his father's debt?

"I tell you, people of Nimo,
Only a fool pursues a bull empty-handed.
The bare-fisted warrior will sooner
Come home in a casket.

"Agubanze, hardly an adult, spoke against me.
Yet a fly is more easily killed than disposed of.
The issue is not giving the monkey a cup of water,
But retrieving the cup from it.
Agubanze, hardly an adult, spoke against me.
The foolish man who suddenly becomes wise
Complains of insomnia.

"Agubanze, hardly an adult, spoke against me.
Is a well-prepared mind not a cracking stone
That crushes the rind of any nut?
And yet the child who draws his father's arrow
At a deer, falls with the deer.

"People of Nimo,
Is a priced cock not known
From the day it hatches?
A bad woman is known from the way
She gathers her breadfruit.
Still a woman who turns her bare buttocks
To a man may not complain of squirty mess.

"Agubanze, hardly an adult, spoke against me.
Would it matter if it is a bird or a *birdling*,
Whichever one of them that wanders into a thorny
Bush will surely lose an eye.
Men may not visit the forest of snakes.
Besides let him who learns to walk like the snake,
Also master his wily ways.
After all the bush that would not accept
All types of baskets may not grow mushrooms.

"Ezenwanmadu, how can I make it clear
That there is no *snakeling* on its fangs.
Every deaf ear dies when the head
Is cut off on its account.
When a misinspired old woman jumps a fence,
Her corpse will be found on the other side.

"People of Nimo,
The monkey's hand must be lifted from the soup pot
Well before it turns into a human hand.
Have you not noticed that the nanny looks on
When its mother is foddering?
Or that the sling with which a child killed
A vulture was made by the adult?
Ezenwammadu, the lion saw me and ran way,
Would your son be the impudent dog that would bark at me?'

'Then Ezenwanmadu said to Izaka,
'The ovoviviparous lizard said
Her husband's relatives tied her womb,
And the dancing snake said its limbs
Are safely tucked away in its stomach.
Unless he is called Izaka,
Can a man suffering from elephantiasis
Boast of a beautiful body?
Unless they are called Izaka,
Do self-respecting men dance to
The sound of their wive's pestles?

Even then, a nesting bird makes out time
To defecate outside its nest.
You that love funeral food,
You must take great care not to die.

"Izaka, Agubanze was young and inexperienced
You should have left him to us.
The mother of a dwarf knows how best to carry him.
Agubanze was an only palm kernel,
How could he possibly get lost in the fire?
But you, Izaka, are the dog that chances
Upon a bone that goes straight to its palms.
You would kill a child without hesitation.

"Izaka, looking at the bearded mouth of an adult,
You would think he never suckled a breast.

"Izaka, when we made similitude of a calf,
Did we ask you to slay its mother?

"Izaka, he who eats the testis of a ram,
Owes a debt to elephantiasis of the scrotum.

"Izaka, listening to the cackle of a hen
That has just laid an egg,
You would think she laid a thousand eggs.
The nails of the lizard do not hurt
The bark of the Iroko tree.
Indeed, like suds is the strength of a child.
Even then, the snake does not swallow
What enters its burrow.

"Izaka, how can an egg eater
Tell if he has eaten a prize cock?'

'Then Izaka replied,
'Ezenwanmadu, the lizard that does not molt
With its mates will become a wild lizard.

The lunacy that enters the market place is incurable.
When the goat that knows the way to the yam barn
Is untethered, it goes straight to the barn.
Besides, you have been known to advise men
To drain the puddle while their feet are still seen.
Ezenwanmadu, have you not noticed
That the man who has just bought a gun
Has a swagger to his steps?
Or are you unaware that a small breeze ignored
Can put out a wild fire?'

'Then Ezenwanmadu said,
'Very well Izaka, let the rat that ate
The pounded yam explain what happened to the soup pot.
If a tick is removed from a dog,
Must it not be shown to him, if not,
Should the dog not assume he was pinched?
My son's speech was both morally sound
And ideologically correct.'

Then Izaka said,
'Very well Ezenwanmadu,
I know that the bird that is always scratching
Its eyes is never satisfied with seeing.
Still I say that the child that eats grasshoppers
Is not only hungry but stupid.
Besides, the snake and its killer are both faced
With the common objectives of longevity.'

'Then in great exasperation, Izaka said,
'Which wise man knows his thing
That would not hold his sting?
Such is he for whom history has no place,
Whose memory will be imperiled by
The passage of time.
For it is not necessary that an upstirring
Be ideologically correct,
But that it be propitiated by circumstances

Presenting, a time-honored alternative
Valid, for such a time as it is not enchaffed.

''Thus, morality becomes an ever-changing concept,
Valid for one age, invalid for another,
And always dredging out frontiers of alternatives.
Thus, the absolute truth is that men,
Constantly battered as it were with uncertainties
Must be constantly bathed in alternatives,
For such is the nature of man.
And that is the essence of the morality of power.
And then, let the threats of war,
The exigencies of survival,
The sheer force of argument
That redefines positions of truth,
Be they that guide an upstirrer
To a successful upstirring.

''Thus, ideological correctness of power
Would not be the moral imperatives,
But the circumstantial imperatives,
Although as it were, one predicates the other.'

'At this point, the elders marveled at the
Wisdom of Izaka. We knew that not even
Ezenwanmadu could upstage him.
I had looked at Nwoye and he
Scratched his long beards in great perplexity.
If ever there was a time he needed palm wine,
It was now.

'Then Izaka continued,
'The gregariousness of which you are aware,
Is the sociology of truth in action.
Men cluster up because they are bound
By a consensus of shared truths,
And a cluster is differentiated from another
Because it is imperative for one to show
That it is held by a higher position of truth.

This highness becomes a halo,
A nebulous shell of light,
From which men unleash self
And group righteousness, seeming.
Thus does insecurity grow clusters,
Glued together by a shared stratagem,
On how to fixate, modify or ameliorate uncertainties,
Thus inspiring racial, tribal, and familial exclosures,
Inspiring classes of all shades and climes,
Inspiring hate, violence and love sublime,
According as is necessary to uphold
Positions of truth or security,
And to ward off threats
Poking at issues, perceivably essential
For survival. Thus is the myth of equalitarianism
Shattered, becoming only a broken platform
From which men imagine the truth
That could have been, and play mind games
With the phantom of circumstances,
Which is the truth seen in as many streaks of light
As observers, the truth that would be.

"The different truth groups
Are not in themselves inimical,
They being like bristles upon
The wheels of civilization that
Guarantee its firm footing.
Thus, the conflict of truths,
Which breeds civilizations, breeds war.
War being the violent displacement
Of one truth by another.

"Very well, let me further educate you
O men of Nimo, that unhappiness
Is an individual's response to anxiety.
The latter being the physiological
Expectation of the outcome of uncertainties,
And the degree of happiness is the expression
Of the utility attached to the favorable

Outcome of probable truth.

"And so, the social man gathers consensus,
And the political man defends the consensus.
And a man or group then seek
To attain their greatest happiness
By minimizing their anxiety levels.
And when men cannot determine their
State of happiness, they lose their freedom.
Since all men desire maximum freedom,
There can be no peace in the community of men.'

'Looking at a distance,
We heard a stirring in the undergrowth
And Izaka angrily bellowed saying,
'The council of gods decree death,
And I am but an instrument of the gods.
There was not so much as one
Whose death was not decreed by the gods.
If it pleases the gods that men may die
On account of their transgression towards me,
So be it, for before the greatness of the gods
I am worth but a trifle.'

'Then Ezenwanmadu replied,
Trembling and retreating,
'Who then fashions out the path
That the gods might follow, for
Councils are erected to smoothen
The dimensions of authority
And of its delivery and to guard
So that anarchy may not burst
Forth in their ranks?

"Do gods live as men do?
Are they motivated by uncertainty and needs
Without which their existence would be futile?
Speak, Izaka, without flare or roaring.
Are the councils then a collective way

To deal with their insecurities?
Speak, for there are hints of
The hierarchicality of power,
For the imperfection of the gods presuppose
A perfect God.'

'At this point, Izaka emerged
From the undergrowth and we fled
To mourn the death of Agubanze.

'While fleeing, we heard Izaka say,
'Men of Nimo, who is brave among you
Let him stand and trade the knowledge
Of motivation and classes with his life.
For like the gods, even a man
Needs, then he wants,
Then he wants to fulfil his needs,
Then he needs to fulfil his wants,
Then his wonts become a need,
And a new array of wants is formed,
While all this time synthesizing
Elaborate truth groups,
That justify their exclusionary mentalities.
All social classes are thus predicated by needs.''

Nwabuno sobbed!
At this point, Nwabuno, still visibly shaken, sat down.
According to legend,
Nwabuno who had an arthritic hip, was least able to flee.
Izaka, caught up with her and
Strangled her. Besides, if ever
There was a thorn on Izaka's side
It was Nwabuno who knew all
Of Izaka's lovers and told.

Then from the village of Otenyi,
Arose Mgbanwkwocha again,
She who is fondly called
'Voice of the weather-beaten gong'

Still decked out in her dancing costume.
She allowed a few steps. Stopped.
The occasion was too solemn
For even an instinctive display.
Looking towards Izaka, she said:

'Izaka, was there ever a story teller
Who could narrate all that you did or said?
Was the revered forest of Ojita
Not your favorite resting place?
There you have been known to hide
At dusk and early dawn, covered
By its magnificent botanical plumage,
Ogling at the women of Ezira
Whose bathing place it was, further down,
At the outlet to Obele nmili.

'Was it not true that sometimes
You let their garments slip into the river,
And you became all the merrier
As you watched their bewilderment,
As they bent in different shapes
Trying to salvage their clothes
From the river's current, providing
You with a fuller view of their
Erogenous zones, while all this
Time stroking your carnality to explosion?

'Nwabuno, whose tongue was
Anchored in slime, of the village of Amafum
Said that once, you saw the
Fat buttocks of the wife of
Nkwobele, the eldest son of Ogbunnugaeke,
And laughed uproariously.
So loud was your amusement
That the breadfruits let go
Of their fruits and the Iroko trees
Shed their leaves, for Nwoyenwa, son of Ayiba,
The sedulous tenderer of goats.

'So loud did you laugh that the oil bean trees
Exploded in deafening clatter; so loud …
Then unbeckoned, you proceeded
To forcibly fondle her buttocks;
So hard … that Azuka, the woman
Of the fat buttocks, the wife of
Nkwobele, the eldest son of
Ogbunnugaeke, left the river in shame
With her earthen pot broken in distress,
And vowed never to come back.

'Two full moons later, she died
Of wounded self-esteem and
Nkwobele, who had been nursing a swollen feet,
Two full moons hence,
Gave up his ghost in frustration.

'Izaka, you were a thorn in the body
Of organized societies. You made more
Mischief than *ogbanje*[24] - the fickle-
Minded children of the river goddess.

'In between several quaffs of palm wine,
Nwoye Akubue of Ezira, the gentle giant
Whose head touches the shoulders
Of the palm tree, whose uncanny ribaldry
Was moistened by kegs of palm wine,
Inebriated as always, but especially
On Oye market days, says of Azuka:

"Whose eyes would not roll in wonderment?
Whose face would not crack up in mirth?
It was big, beyond what even Izaka
Could contemplate, so big was her buttocks
That two full measures of Ojita
Could not wash it clean,
So fleshy, it was little wonder that
Nkwobele, (fatuous as ever, never seemed
To have enough to eat) seemed like the

Tendrils of the widow's yam.
So watery, it was the stuff of which
Adolescent males make their fantasies.
Who would blame Izaka, a merry man beyond
Reproach?'

'Even Okeke Ifezue, the serious-faced
Blacksmith of whom it was said
That he had pieces of iron welded
Into his face, let a smile slip through
His bearded mouth.

'Izaka, where were you
When the white man came to ravage
The great and magnificent forest of Ojita?
Magnificent for centuries before the white man
Was made. Greatly endowed, better than any forest
Of its kind. Ojita was worthy enough to be
The gathering grounds of the greater spirits.
Ojita, where the first man was made
And the first species of any kind was born.
So unique, so beautiful, so evolutionarily
Significant, that Ezenwanmadu, who spoke
The language of spirits, said it was the navel,
Once bearer of the umbilical chord,
Through which heaven shed its contents on earth.

'Izaka, you told the white man about Ojita,
He called it Eden.
You told him about the beauty of Ojita,
He called it paradise.
But you lied about how you desecrated it.
You said a woman consummated of its beauty
And paradise fell.
But it was you Izaka, who desecrated
The hallow grounds of Ojita.
Izaka of the dubious legend,
How you have ruined the course of history!

'Nwaolise, the estranged son of Ebube,
The last of the great oral historians said
That after the death of Azuka,
The women of Ezira learnt to hide
Their bodies from you, and completely denied
You your voyeuristic amusement
And you swore in anger to punish the black man.
And in anger, you finally took off to a cold
And strange land, to Mount Olympus,
According to the revelations of Okonkwo, the drummer,
With Mgbankwocha, the albino of Umudunu,[25]
And you made for yourself a strange people,
Upon whom you imbued your sense of treachery
And mischief and imbued in them
Your love of lewdity and your obsession
With sex and sexual organs
And you thought them the secrets of
Our people and you charged them
To destroy, take slaves, and plunder.

'Izaka, has not your temperament
Ruined history for mankind?
What an abomination, in support
Of your untamable excesses.'

Then looking up again,
I saw Nwabuno, decked out in black and gold
And eagle's feather.
She had assumed center stage again.
She said in a mellowed voice:

'Izaka was our heart and soul;
When he left, we lost our heart and soul.
Izaka's exploits were like the shady ramparts
Of Ukpakaegbutunma,[26] underneath which
We built Ogwenso,[27] and traded our experiences.
When he left, the logs were dispersed
And with them, the bonds of brotherhood.

'Izaka was the restraining rope
As of the big masquerade
That held us within those bounds of brotherhood,
When he left, the center went asunder,
And we have already sung his homecoming.

'What juicy stories he made,
How dry the way that laid ahead.
About Izakaocha, Nwoyeizaka, and all
The princely bastards that littered our villages,
Even a reptile is more mindful of its young ones
For no man sends his own children on late-night errands.

'O how we relished his sweet absurdities.
What fondness lit the eyes of our youth,
When the elders narrated the marvelous deeds
He wrought. O, how with the exuberance of youth,
Our males recalled his match of wits
With Ezenwanmadu, and our females harbored
Dreams of men with Izaka's stamina.

'Izaka, when you left,
The blacksmiths sprung up everywhere
Like cocoyam planted by evil spirits
And the ways of arms became our ways.
Mighty men who were humbled by your might,
And violent men who were dismayed
By your ferocity, sprung up, arms in tow
With long knives girded around their waists,
To unruly adventurism, and left victims
In their wake, like a bad fairy tale.

'Night by night, we heard
The deep-throbbing sounds of war drums
And our villages were overcast by the cloud of war.

'There was reserve on every face.
Men lost faith in their wives,

And the tortuous path to Ojita
Was no longer graced by the
Deliberate, unhurried and cheerful
Steps of our women, and the
Countenances of our children
Were sour like a spoilt melon soup.

'Izaka, it is true you smeared
Your ego on every mind,
But the fear of the gods
Restrained our errant minds.

'Izaka, some said, come back
So that the warriors and the warfarers
May sleep, for you represented an ultimate in
Strength that for men,
Obviated exhibitionism of any kind.

'Was this not Izaka,
Before whom we processed with festal shouts?
And we stood in reverence
When Ebenebe said,
'Give us strength, give us wisdom
Guide us and uphold our laws
Give us rain to soften the tiller's ground.'

'Was this not Izaka
Before whom we processed with festal shouts?
Upon whose excesses we regulated our lives,
And upon whom our widows pledged
Their bonds of love.

'Izaka, with teary hearts and heavy hearts,
We said, 'May greatness be with you,
May you go on to seed other civilizations.'
Izaka, what you wrought upon us was beyond pardon.
Who could understand your relationship with us?

'Was this not Izaka,

Before whom we processed with festal shouts?
About whom the historians said,
'He was as vagarious as clouds
In the rainy season.'

Was this not Izaka, whose portraits of virility
Our wives carried in their hearts,
Upon whose deeds of valor we modeled our young males?
Izaka, how could you drive a knife into us so
And made us victims of your excesses?
Izaka, the evil you wrought upon us
Was beyond pardon.

'Ebenebe, your principal consort,
The custodian of the rain forest says,
'It is crying time, our hearts are heavy.'
And so it is.'
At this point, the whole village arose
Man, woman, child and beast.
The mood was somber.
The verdict had been perceived.
Izaka was to die.

From their midst, I heard the seasoned
Voice of an elder, Ezenwanmadu's, saying,
'Izaka whom we despised,
Did they not call you Zeus?
And Okonkwo the legendary drummer-poet
They called, Euhemerus?

We mourn Ojita,
We lament its loss,
We mourn the loss of that great relic,
Reminder of our benign association with nature,
Before the white man desecrated it
At your own behest.
Izaka, how could you alienate us
From our principal source of pride -

The great and awe-inspiring forest of Ojita.'

So saying, the assembly stilled,
And a great mist rolled into their camp.
After what seemed like eternity,
Everybody still standing,
Izaka spoke saying:

'Before you, mother,
Before your majestic presence,
Before this assizes
Of the great Nimo people
Who have justly robed me in their contempt,
Surrounded by the assurgent mist of your laws,
Guilty I stand, of my deeds,
Presumptuous and consensual.

'Accused by myself the accuser,
Agitated I stand, drooling
Of the blood of my rebellion.

'I am Izaka.
Under the weight of my indulgent pride,
I became the center that splintered,
The foothold that yielded,
The lifeline that snapped,
The cornerstone that buckled.
I, who am given to whims,
Caprices and extensive freeplay,
Who supplanted discipline with lewdism.
I, of the egregious carnal appetite,
The fly that could not avoid the slaughterhouse.

'I am the star who said to the star maker,
'I have outshone you,
I am established way above you.'
I forgot even in the midst of
Constant reminders and raised arms

To my own embattlement.

'I am the mountain
Who said to the mountain maker,
'My summit is beyond your reach,
I desire only to frolic with
The highest heavens. I, who am
Most beautiful, vain and proud,
I desire that no one else may
Take pleasure in me, but
I in all and at odds with you.'

'I am the bubble who said to the bubble maker
'Burst me if you can!'

'I am Izaka, dweller in the clouds,
Then at Ojita, then at Olympus,
Until the truth was revealed to men
And godship became a dubious legend.

'I am the mighty sea
Who billowed my way
Through the frontiers of men's naivete,
And raised arbitrary standards in their midst
Thereby severely distorting the truths
Which must be held high,
Configuring them to perpetual warfare and discord.

'I am Izaka of the mighty phallus,
The burning spear,
Whom all women awaited, and all men envied.
Who made love with equestrian intensity
And mocked the swift
And walked in thunder's path;
Whose baptism of fire was rendered
Only on creation's day.

'I, an only mountain

Imposing and awe-inspiring,
The stow, the crest, I had it all …
The spirits, the men …
Even the great courage of your divine mandate…
On what omen might blame be laid?

'Today, justice glowers.
Their testimonies inveigh me,
Their wailing, the infant's cry,
The moans of the adult,
The widows' cry
Cries of bereaved children whose fathers I destroyed,
The whining of the homeless dog,
They all cry ill of me.

'Hence, I come, profligate
In all my beauty and pride, to the
Guillotine bound, where like
The Indian thunderbird that
Would no longer grace the trail of tears,
The African warrior, frenzied and intense,
The extinct cultures, banished from the present
Never to be reclaimed; like Ikenga,
Symbol of their ancestral ties,
Like Nwoye Ajagu of Ajanzo,
The last of the great wine tapsters of Nimo,
Like the Akwete clothe that dies in all its beauty,
Like the goat whose fate is sealed in sacrifice,
I, having attained my ignoble end,
In all my hubris, I must die.'

So saying, Izaka was led off.
The mist vanished and the people dispersed
To the accompaniment of solemn drum beats.
At this time, a woman began to weep.
It was Nwanyiekie of Amafum,
Izaka's favorite lover,
Renowned for her beauty and grace.

'Here might I stay,' she wept
'And sing no story so sorrowful,
Never did a soul so profoundly feel,
The agony of hate and death.
Death has no handsome face,
The thoughts of dreams forever deferred,
Of love that meets its frigid terminus,
Laughter frozen in midstream
And dignity that soon splinters
Into a thousand maggots.
O death, you have no handsome face.

'O death, O tyrannical one,
How cruel the means by which you attain
Your necessary ends.
For without you, no birth can be justified.
Would that you were neither ugly nor arbitrary,
Would that you were not cruelly kind,
Would rites, spring, of renewal not
Be properly presaged?
O death, you have no handsome face.'

'O mother of justice
There is no good way to kill a man,
Not even one deserving death.
There is no kind killing, no mercy death,
There is no neat way to kill a man.
O mother of justice and mankind,
Is it not more proper to let die than to kill?'

Not to be outdone, Nwabuno said,
'O mother of justice, Izaka is a soiled water
That must be poured away.
If an animal runs carelessly, it is shot carelessly.
The planter of cassava does not harvest cocoyam.
When a man throws a stone into a crowded market place,
It is only fair that it lands on his mother.
When a trader passes off sand as salt

Should she not receive pebbles as money?
As to the manner of punishment, we know
That a dog does not select its own name –
It is what the master calls him that he answers.'

Then turning towards the guillotine
She said with all the passion in her voice,
'O mother of justice,
It is only fair that a seat should await a pair of buttocks.'

The heavens were silent.
The people had all disappeared
And the drummers held their drums.
Nwanyiekie's sobbing voice resounded
Throughout the heavens.

'*Ewuuu Chimu!*' She sobbed.

Drumbeat! Drumbeat!

Endnotes

[1] Izaka had a habit of being extremely solicitous of widows. Those who spurn his attention are reminded that his help was obligatory.

[2] god of fire, patron of blacksmiths.

[3] A precinct of Nimo.

[4] Otuba was disappointed to learn that "his" daughter was Izaka's daughter after all.

[5] Egwuatu's well was very productive and produced the clearest water. It was said that his water was specially cleansed by the spirits he consulted and he charged for water drawn from his well. When Egwuatu drowned in that well, it was never visited again and the people of Umueze have not forgiven Izaka over the years.

[6] A precinct of Nimo.

[7] A precinct of Nimo.

[8] Titular ruler of Nimo.

[9] A sacred tree that must never be cut or trimmed.

[10] One of the four main subdivisions of Nimo.

[11] A precinct of Nimo.

[12] One of the four main subdivisions of Nimo.

[13] A precinct of Nimo.

[14] A precinct of Nimo.

[15] A precinct of Nimo.

[16] A precinct of Nimo.

[17] Izaka's favorite lover.

[18] A precinct of Nimo.

[19] A precinct of Nimo.

[20] Ezenwanmadu's second and favorite son. He was about twenty four years old at the time of this celebrated speech. Izaka killed him shortly afterwards. Agubanze married Ebenebe's first daughter. This author is a direct descendant of Agubanze.

[21] Among the Igbos, markets days are held in four-day cycles, namely Oye, Afo, Nkwo and Eke.

[22] Izaka was implying that Agubanze must have been asked by the elders to deliver his damning speech.

[23] Izaka is saying that if a young man of twenty four could be that powerful, imagine how he would be as he gains more wisdom.

[24] Ogbanje were children who traverse a revolving door between life and death.

[25] A precinct of Nimo.

[26] A sacred tree that may not be cut or trimmed.

[27] A step-wise seating arrangement. A favorite hang out for men of all age groups. Here men traded stories and tapsters returning from the swamps stopped by to have their wines interpreted. On market days, men typically gathered here and quaffed down endless gulps of palmwine. According to Nwoye, it was under circumstances such as this that glorious thoughts were hatched and tribology of friendship enhanced.

Chapter 15

A Child's Well Spring Of Gratitude

True liberty, in life or death,
Liberty and pride shall be
My watchword at heaven's gate.
On the day we meet again,
On fishing day, at the junction
Of the seven seas, may it be said,
'He planted love's flag in every heart,'
And bid them, 'flap with joy,
Affirm our oneness.'
Let the joy of brotherhood
Be the theme of the glory song.

Six months had elapsed since
I witnessed the homecoming of Izaka.
By now my days were filled with
A quiet re-examination of the nature
Of man, of love, hate, classism,
And all his motivating instincts.

I sought philosophical justification
For the segregative nature of men.
'The bat,' I rationalized, 'accepted its ugliness,
Made peace with himself, and chose the night.'
'The cow,' I further rationalized, 'follows his master
In the interest of peace and not because it fears
A contest of strength.'

With each quiet resolution of acceptance,
I felt more and more spiritually emasculated.
I had followed Willie's bidding
And was by now residing in Georgia.
I had been to the projects
And had toured the predominantly black
Neighborhoods. I was struck by the
Hopelessness that hung all around them.
I felt the earth in Georgia, and
Recalled Willie's biding,
Which was becoming quite unsettling.
For he had said, 'For Georgia has neglected
To erect memorials to black men lynched on
Her soil. Please sir, do not let us die.'

I resolved to tell this story. But first,
I needed answers.
At the heel of one Saturday's dawn,
I felt myself slipping through that small window
That marks a change in animistic frequency,
A state of controlled thoughtlessness,
A physiological quiet accompanied
By a blank cartridge;

Then, I felt the familiar presence of Nwoye,
That benign and legendary free bird.

'Nwoye,' I groped.

'Son, the flying kite has a shadow on the ground.'

'What?'

'An errand sent by way of smoke
Has already reached the heavens.'

'Nwoye, the breadfruit that fruited on the day we were
Wondering if it would ever do so, did not fruit on time.'

'Son, many are the friends of the storyteller,
But it is cowardly to seek an escort
Back to one's home.
The brilliance of the moon
Does not alter the character of the night.
Have you not heard that there is no river
For which there is no suitable boat?
Even then, when the next step is not obvious
Men must take the obvious next step.
Is there a feared idol that is not tended by a man?'

Then I replied,
'If pounded yam were not afraid
Of its journey to the stomach,
Would it ask vegetables to accompany it?
Would you urge a man who finally
Climbs an Iroko tree not to fetch firewood?'

'No, but I am afraid that a child
Who is told tales of war itches for a confrontation.'

'Yes, but a child whose mother has not come back
Insists that the market place is not yet closed.
Nwoye, you are to me like an experienced medicine man

You talk directly to the ears of the spirits.'

'Nwoye of the merry man's paradox,
Why does the caged bird bother to sing?'

'Son, the caged bird sings
Not so its captors might release her,
But so the world may hear and bear witness
To the suppression of one creature by another.'

'Very well, why, O free bird
Does the caged bird grow not fat? I hear,
Legend says, your brilliant mind
Is caged in palm wine, yet you are
Freer than all free men.'

'Dim wits!
The vulture may braid her hair
But as to the coronation ceremony,
She is still not invited.
The bird knows why it has no testis
Dangling outside its body.
The indigent widow claims she dislikes
The taste of meat.
When a bad cook overseasons her food,
She claims it was at the recommendation of
The medicine man.
When a newlywed cooks bad dishes,
She claims she must pander to her fetus' taste.
Say, when will you stop achieving the glitter
In men's eyes and achieve that which is most
Fundamental- happiness? Nwoye may be caged
By palm wine but he is free and happy.'

Nwoye had evaded my question-
Obviously I had leaned on a sore spot.

'Ha ha he ha ha hee,' Nwoye laughed.

'What now, O self-indulgent free bird?
Is that the self-apprehensive smile
Of the embarrassed? Is that a genuine smile
Or the wry smile of a dog that was served a roasted yam?
Nwoye, I am reminded that we do not direct
A caress in the neighborhood of a wound.'

'Son, when a woman scratches her pubic zone
She has a tendency to smile alone.'

Chuckle!

'Son, a child who laughs at his father's rotten yam
Laughs at his impending hunger!'

'What?' I asked, enjoying Nwoye on the defensive
A rare feat if ever there was one.
This was after all Nwoye, the legendary free bird!

'A child who laughs at his mother's flat buttocks
Laughs at his father,' Nwoye replied.

'What?' Pressing the issue.

'A child who calls his father's wife a thief
Calls his mother a thief.'

'An itch in that area of the body is insuperable.
When a woman smiles alone, did she scratch
Her pubic zone?' I asked.

'Probably,' Sounding reluctant to pursue that point.

'Very well Nwoye,' I finally said,
'Smile is the landscape of laughter,
And laughter, the first fruit of happiness.
But if Noah must get drunk,
Should he not guide his loincloth?'

'Nwoye, you who is versed in the anatomy of humor,
How often you remind me that a mad man may be cured
But for his habit of murmuring.
Nwoye, how did beautiful women affect you?'

'Son, I saw sexual intemperances,
The swirling of testicles,
The hardening of eyeballs,
Unidirectional gaze,
The gushing of blood,
The stirring of juices,
Emotional waterfalls that
Rearranged the axes of my thoughts,
In short, senses gone wild.'

'Nwoye, I did not ask you all that.
Very well, tell me the anecdote of the he-goat.'

'Son, when the randy he-goat
Was asked where he had been, looking up,
He sneered, let out a self-satisfied smile
And said, 'How many times should I tell you
That in my grandmother's family, I have
A thousand concubines?'
'What a splash,' he added, and set out again.'

Chuckle!

'Son, what has become of the people of Nimo?'

'Men of Nimo are living out their dreams still,
Only a vastly different dream,
To the degrees of their inspiration,
To the interpretations of the priests
Of the Western god.
May their hearts be inflamed by true passion.

'We welcomed change
May change not be our bane.'

'And about the maidens of Nimo?'

They have gone wild.
They have taken to the white man's fascination
With upraised buttocks and painted lips.
And they now shoot birds,
That do not perch on their arrowheads.'

'And the society we left to your care?'

'Nwoye, our values have become monetized,
Fast money and fat prostitutes are bedding furiously…
Gun-totting Generals and bloody-eyed politicians…
Loud-mouthed pimps are making brisk business…
In the von Karman boulevard of our corruption.'

'Son, what say you of Western culture?'

'They love to make tornadoes,
And then attempt to arrest them with a big net.
Then they try to clone a wooly mammoth
To see if it can be arrested by a mouse trap.
Then they release the mammoth on the society
And make money selling new and improved mouse traps.
And the capital generated is used to fund
Much glitz, tall hotels, snoot and foppery,
Policemen exhibiting arrogance and maximum,
All accented by the swagger of high-heeled women.

And smog, smog in the skyline,
Smog in my mind,
Smog ubiquitously clouding
The horizons of my thoughts;
My depleted lungs yell, smog!'

'Nwoye, what may I say to the Westerner?'

'Son, admonish the white man to
Not desecrate the land because he is on top of a tree
For when the heavens fall, the trees will fall.
Caution him that a bird may wish to die in the sky
But the earth shall be the ultimate repose of its bones
For what befalls one will surely befall another.'

'Son, how about the good workers of the West?'

'Among them, conformity is almost everything,
Performance is lightly treasured in comparison,
And the boss is life itself.
And the labor unions, the master's tragedy.'

'Nwoye, why do the gods ignore your scurrility?'

'Son, if the world were stupid,
Some men would claim sweet smelling feces.
A man's ego is well served
Who has performed a satisfying act of sex,
But a man would not be immodest
Who is reminded of the anticlimax
Following an ejaculation.
Son, my unspeakable realities are but prods
That cleanse the rotten core of men.'

'Very well, Nwoye, why do you eat your words
With so much palm oil?'

'Son, proverbs instruct the wise,
The foolish flee in confusion.
Basically, to distinguish the men from the boys.
The elders may not be profligate with words.
A tiny vibrant string of poignant imagery
Is worth a hundred spoken days of platitudes.
Words packaged in images is the mark

Of a seasoned title man.
The tone and sound of words, brevity displayed,
Is a pleasure to the senses.
Besides, a flippant elder is a profanity
To their institution.'

'Nwoye of the merry man's paradox,
Tell me about the drum.'

'One mouth disseminates caustic verbiage,
The other disseminates rhythm and harmony,
And belches into the universe, charm,
That soothes the savage in men.

'Son, who but a mad man
Will abandon a feast for a sanatorium?
The reason why we pound yams
Is not because the mortar is a better
Masticator than the teeth, but so
We will find excuses to gulp down
Long and juicy strands of bitterleaf soup.

'Son, we talk with the talking drum,
Its cryptic verbiage,
Only known to a select few.'

Nwoye, although a drunk,
Was perhaps the greatest abstract thinker
Of his time. I had decided to use my isolation with him
To probe his deepest insight. I began:

'Nwoye, what is good?'

'Good is merely the standard
By which evil is to be condemned.'

'And truth?'

'There is no truth but the liar's truth,
It is in the unknowability of the truth
That lies its essence.
Truth is the obverse of falsity,
Both are indeterminable'

'And life?'

'Life and death are the two sides of a coin.
Of the other, one is a mere consequence,
For life renews death renews life,
And they both define an existence
Material or immaterial.'

'And existence?'

'Existence is the mere notion that arises
When one imbeds the concept of initiation
And termination unto any contrived truth or objective.'

'And you, do you exist?'

'Since I began, then I exist.
Since I exist, then I must cease existing
And yet, all existence is a mere notion.'

'And of Nwoye in the flesh?'

'The flesh is the actuator for the consciousness.
Within one existence, are but numerous subexistences-
All driven by the same core consciousness.
The predominant subexistence
Modulates the activities of the core consciousness,
Which in turn is a repository of all the information
Needed for survival at any existence level or sublevel.
Thus, birth and death are simultaneous occurrences
Accomplishing the transition from one subexistence to
another.'

'And God?'

'Son, God exists only if he were a notion,
For again all existence is a mere notion.
And so, God does not exist
In time, truth, and space coordinates.
His existence is not phenomenological,
Cannot be proven, comprehended or subjected
To any linear logical expostulations
For all else exists but for God
Who is neither a notion nor has an initiation nor a termination.
But only a fool says there is no God.'

'But Nwoye, how did God arise?
Can something arise out of nothing?
Am I and my world, not an illusion
As surely as my God is an illusion?'

'Son, which is more logically intact?
That in the very beginning there was nothing
Or that in the very beginning there was something?
The existence of something out of nothing occurs
By the principle of transrealization,
Involving the embedment of real time frame unto
An apparent nothing.'

'Son, the apparent reality of a dream state,
Is a transrealized state.'

'So Nwoye, that which arises out of nothing is nothing.
But nothing can be transrealized,
Giving rise to apparent reality or illusion.
If, therefore, in the beginning there was nothing,
Then nothing can arise out of nothing that is something.'

'Son, but nothing is simply something for which nothing else
Can be compared. Recall he says, 'I am who am,'
Implying his incomparableness.

So in the beginning, there was he,
That was nothing,
That is our God,
And everything else exists in the transrealized
Consciousness of God
All of existence, mere notions all,
Exist in the transrealized consciousness of God.

With the word, he accomplished his transrealization.
And that word was God's total awareness of himself.
So in the beginning was also the word,
And that was with God,
And that was God.

'That which has neither a beginning nor an ending
Must be nothing, which is our God.
Thus is God's immortality explained.
But Nwoye, how about the end of time?

'Son, when the element of time is dissociated
From something, it becomes nothing, immaterial
Or amaterial, having no comparative base -
A thing is because it is not another.
Since the word which is the medium of transrealization
Is a function of time, at the end of time,
It would cease to exist
And everything else will collapse to
The glorious nothingness of God.'

'Again son, I warn you,
That the dimensions of a system are its unique
And independent attributes.
A well-defined system is one that is fully dimensionalized.
Only a fool attempts to define God.
The knowledge of whom
Cannot be subjected to linear argumentation,
And the dimensionality of a man's world is far too limited
To appreciate the nature of God.

Suffice it to add that the God, which is felt at any
Existence level, is merely an idealized projection
Of the unique attributes of that level.'

'Nwoye, how you mock my wit so.
Should it be said that your hand withered
Before it reached a child's mouth?'

'Son, knowledge is a big burden,
Its first son is cynicism.'

'Nwoye, give a bone to a dog
Forget about its fight with the spirits.'

'Very well son,
Contrast is the first law of existability
And finitude, the impermanence of all states,
Is its second and final law and that which
Is infinite is only finitely so.'

'Nwoye?'

'Son, all that is finite is a manifestation of the infinite.'

'With what then do you contrast the infinite?'

'With all that is finite.'

'And the end of the infinite?'

'The improbable end of all that is finite.
All finite forms exist within an infinite envelope.
There is that immanence of the infinite in all forms,
A conceptual web, originating from the envelope,
Connecting all finite forms,
And terminating on the envelope.'

'Nwoye, you torment me so.'

'Son, the spirit of a man is merely a field of force.
The soul is the generator of the spirit.
And the flesh is the housing of the generator.
Only the flesh is temporal.
The flesh modulates the soul.
The soul is a node on the web of existence.
The flesh dies when dissociated from the soul.
The spirit acts through the flesh
And the flesh through the spirit.
A hysteresis exists.
The activities of the flesh yield information.
The goal of the soul is to be perfectly informed,
To act in a universally rational manner.
The more informed soul is the greater soul.
The soul is amorphous and takes the shape
Of the object within which it resides.'

'Is there a materiality to every soul?'

'Yes. But materiality is a function of its existence level.'

'Nwoye, you would not blame a thirsty wayfarer
Who attempts to fill his gourd upon encountering an oasis?'

'No, son. But it is much easier to drain the ocean into
A palm kernel's nut than to understand the nature of God.
And then, there is the huge translational effort in relating
The little I know to the nothing you know.'

'Very well Nwoye,
What is your commentary on religion?'

'Son, a man who has attained the virtues of patience,
Humility, kindness and good industry,
Has no need for conversion.
All religions are good to the extent that they help men
Attain these, hence, helping to maintain social decorum.
And then, for evolutionary progression,

One must fully understand the universalism
And unitariness of God. Any teaching beyond this
Is blinkered and self serving.'

'And the virtue of patience?'

'A man is patient who is willing to suffer
God's will against the mandate of his spirit.
A man cannot be patient who is not humble.
There is cadence in chaos
And order in randomness.
Nothing happens that was not willed by God.
Be patient then and refrain from self pity
In whatever state or station.'

'And the religious?'

'They must dance to God's values
And walk to his rhythm.
For all such are enslaved to him,
Even though heavily burdened,
He makes free.'

'What are God's values?'

'The values of God are based on the precept
That all of God's children must be left
To unencumberedly pursue his will.'

'And the rhythm of God?'

'God's time is best.'

'How can a man tell God's time?'

'Be patient.'

'Nwoye, you bewilder me.
Should a man vegetate or

Should we live as animals do.
In what may a man exercise his
Natural ability to effect change?
Can a man at least covet
The basic necessities of life?'

'Son, you may not covet food, shelter nor clothing
Nor children, wives, nor parents.
That which he covets burdens a man.
No man can be free who covets anything
But the love of God.'

'Very well Nwoye,
What is your commentary on war?'

'Son, war is an evil justified by necessity,
But only of the imperatives of survival.
Only a vulture sees good in war;
The painful scars of which remain
Long after its lesions are gone.
War is a wound that never truly heals.'

Nwoye was interrupted by the entrance
Of Ezenwanmadu, and Ebenebe and Nwabuno,
And of course, Okonkwo the drummer poet.
Excited, I began,

'O mystery fellows, what tidings have you today,
Will you continue to mock the toils
Of syllable-counters and men who insist that
A game must be properly played to be properly enjoyed?'

Ebenebe said,
'A normal child overwhelmed by gifts
Asks if they belong to someone else, but not this one.'

'Father of my mother,' I said to Ebenebe,
'A hungry man sometimes commits to a meal

Without seeing the contents of the pot.
Even a well-prepared dog meat has its eager takers.'

'But an inquisitive monkey stops a bullet,' Nwoye said.

'No, Nwoye, I am eager and in great haste,
I have no time to admire the monkeys.
Only let it not be said that the rainmaker died
Before he finished his routines.'

'Son,' Ezenwanmadu said,
'Do not lick your fingers in haste
If they will not be tucked beyond your reach.'

Nwabuno, not one to dillydally, said,
'Let us not carry this child on our backs
And let his legs scrape the floor.
This old branch remembers when it was just a bud.
Then we were advised that a chicken's mouthful
Was accompanied by a grain of sand.
But his generation is one without elders,
For them, a vulture has become a hawk.'

The drummer replied, cheerfully,
'Yes, we have come with a basket of words,
And two baskets of proverbs,
And three baskets of similitude,
And four baskets of anecdotes,
Along with a wordsmith if need be,
And we will spray them upon the fertile soil,
So that, like *inine,*[1] they may germinate to
The glory of the gift of language.
And when the vegetable sauce begins to taste good,
We will slice in bits of well-boiled yam,
Otherwise, we will pass the rest to the widow's son
And let her mother think good of us.'

Then Ezenwanmadu said in reference to Nwoye,
'The sole of the feet leads the path.'

Nwoye replied,
'No, the leading rodent may be first to enter a hole.'

And Ebenebe concurred,
'Yes, he who is first to observe
That the vulture is edible may
Be the first to take a bite.'

Clearing his throat, Ezenwanmadu said,
'Well, the leading cattle drinks the clearest water.
We welcome strong wind,
How else could we see the cloaca of the free bird?
Now that we have felt his iron dress,
We believe that the tortoise's claim
Of special endowment is true.

'A man who pays off his debts
Carries a new bag.
Son of his father, you are not a bad dancer
That would bruise the skin of the earth.
Seeing as you now know yourself,
When will your legs again caress
The earth beneath your feet,
And lay your weight upon
The source of your life
Without anger, bitterness or strife,
And dance to the revolutionary rhythm
That was instilled in you?'

The drummer hinted,
'Rejoice, rejoice, O New Jerusalem
For your king shall come to you
O new Israel.'

Then I *replied,*
'Father of his son,
When the king comes home
Amidst pomp and pageantry,
Accompanied by drum beaters,
Relentless rhythm makers,
And by flutists of exquisite skills,
Nimble of lips and hands,
And by sleight-footed dancers
Of mystifying adroitness,
And by the dead who would
Return to life to roost,
Who can resist the urge to dance?

'When Uvoko the flutist calls,
Who will not answer?
I hear the drummer,
Making rhythm of my younger days.
And I recall that when our maidens danced,
When their breasts shook in the moonlight,
Our married men ate their saliva,
With distended eyes and heavy breath,
They rattled in speech.
And our young men shifted uncomfortably
To contain the gyrating exuberance
Of their testicles. Among them,
There was a murmuring, a gentle stirring
As they slipped to the shadows
To hide the bulge they bore.

'When Nwailogi, the legendary dancer
Stamps her first foot,
Accenting the bulgy firmness of her stomach,
Chains of anger are loosened.
When she stamps her second foot,
Taking care to magnify her grace,
Smile trickles down on every face.
And when she lifts herself up in the air,

Letting the rhythmic wave glide
Through every fiber of her femininity,
Catharsis sweeps forth in every rank,
Accompanied by wild clanging applause,
Drowning out the bray of disgruntled womenfolk.

'Father of his son,
Can we skilled in the art of medication
Alienate ourselves from the rhythm of the drum?
It would not be us. No, not us,
The dancers of the rain forest.
Therefore, soon will I dance,
At the latest on the day of
My mother's funeral.
Soon will Uvoko call,
Then, I shall arise to meet the drummer,
And dance in the corridors of ecstasy,
Where under the mellifluous union of
Mind and body, will I not be affrayed,
By me, myself.'

'Then given a nose, snort.
Go, son of his father,
With inertia banished
And routine of fear abolished.
Go, for it was never our style
To worry about death and about
How our corpses might be disposed
By those for whom we died.

'Go with courage blind and
Instincts emboldened by freedom songs.
Go where free men dare,
And shun the clammy palms of bigot's smirk,
And savor with humble relish
All manners of equity and justice.

'Be neither afraid to ask nor to learn
Nor to raise great debates, nor to act well,
For clarity is more enduring than consensus
And good conflicts more divine than bad harmony,
And minor deeds better than the grandest thoughts.

'Go with heart touched by fire.
The handshake that exceeds
An elbow is war declared.
The fight that enters a father's house
Admits no deserters.

'Go, the drums of war are here,
And men must stand apart from the boys.'

'Father of his son,
Was the old and weary dog
Not urged to sleep on a raised platform?
Did he not justifiably state
That he was accustomed to the bare
Thighs of the floor?
Is not it in vain,
That old men strive for ambidexterity?
I am like the water yam,
Too much for any small fire.
An outstander, like the Iroko tree,
I cannot hide nor be hidden,
Adversities flock to me and
Like that mighty tree,
I shake adversities that shake me.
But only an insane bird prays for a rainstorm.'

'Son of his father,
An indecisive hunter
May not dream of big games.
Have they dared the shrine,
Those for whom the wings of flight press on?
Of those who bury themselves,

Something objectionable is always seen,
One hand out of the ground popped.

'Son, man will his greatest enigma always be.
But thanks to time, like grass that covers all.

'Go with diligent mind,
Let time unfurl itself.

'Jump, like solitary waves, run.
Fear not of amplitude damping,
But beware of cliffs and waters' edges
Whereupon come crashing all the waves.'

'Farewell, son of his father,
On hunting day, let us meet
At the homestead of the seven grass cutters.'

Then Ebenebe said in reference to Ezenwanmadu,
'A grass cutter reminded how to bite, bites.
The adult who asks a child to catch a skunk
Must provide a suitable abluent.'

Ezenwanmadu replied,
'Should you ask *nwanza*, the tiny bird
Not to be prepared,
Would it be easier to restrain the wind
That might carry it?
My son will not be like the weakling
Who saw his first corpse in war and
Declared an end to his fighting days.'

Ebenebe said,
'Falling in play is not cowardly.
Recall the squirrel advised walkers to include
Spurts of running should they be required to run.'

'Ebenebe,' I said,

'Were you not called the overscruplous ewe
That would not grow horns?
An adult is not advised to seek shelter from the sun.
A tree that refuses to dance will be taught by the wind.
Truly, only the ear hears of its impending doom
And still rests in its place.
As the layout of a feast changes,
We will adjust our seating accordingly.'

'Son of his mother,
It is best for a single person
To not eat left over food.
Let the child burnt by fire, learn.
A man who stands close enough to a cheek
Can surely slap it.'

'Father of my mother,
Hunger is the platter with which
We accepted unpalatable food.
Yet, should I eat the giant grass in hunger, am I a cow?
Is water not the life of a fish?'

'Son of his mother,
An overfed weaverbird challenges its god
To a wrestling match.
The child who proves too strong may be asked to steal.
A fly rejoices at the sight of newly laid feces,
But clearly, it is soon overwhelmed.'

Nwabuno intervened,
'A man who cannot fight admits guilt
When he is not.
Let him be, for a swimmer
Knows not to swim in the soup pot.
Let him be, for surely he knows
That one who wants to paddle canoe for a living
Should first become a good swimmer.
Surely he knows that a pepper plant is not climbed

And that a crown-wearing king is not slapped,
Not even by the king maker.
Lather or not,
Let him wash his clothes.
I would not advise a child to rest
When there is a hill yet to climb.'

'Nwabuno,' Ebenebe said,
'I merely stated that
He who stands up must be clear
About where he is going.
When too much strength is attributed to a man,
He attempts to lift a house
We do not wish a man a long life
And ignore if he gives little care to living well.'

Then Ebenebe turned towards me and said,
'Farewell, son of his mother,[2]
To freedom, there are no short cuts
Although a fool may make the wrong turn
More than once and may never get there.
The lizard who ignores the tree,
Makes an easy quarry for the dog.
The deaf grasshopper finds repose
In the gizzard of a bird,
Much as the mind which contemplates
Blind confrontation fetches an assassin's bullet.
Only a tree stares motionless at
Its impending death,
Silently he watches the mower,
With each stroke it winches,
As it stoically accepts the fate
Of its passionless existence.'

'Farewell, father of my father's mother,
Custodian of the rain forest.
Whatever is necessary must be
Necessarily done, and that which is just

Must be justly done.
The eye that sees no violence,
Knows no violence.
The eye that turns away from evil, is an accomplice.
It is better that an assassin's bullet
Be my remembrancer than an aged
Life filled with starch and grits.
Indeed, what does it matter to a dead fowl
Who and how her feathers are plucked?
Men of restraint and moderation
Compromise too quickly.

'Father of my mother,
It shall not be said
That I compromised too quickly,
That I exercised patience
With men who assail freedom and usurp peace.

'True liberty, in life or death,
Liberty and pride shall be
My watchword at heaven's gate.
On the day we meet again,
On fishing day, at the junction
Of the seven seas, may it be said,
'He planted love's flag in every heart,'
And bid them, 'flap with joy,'
Affirm our oneness
Let the joy of brotherhood
Be the theme of the glory song.'

'Ebenebe, it shall be well with us.
We have withstood the eye of the storm
And the gods' rage has ebbed.
To us, through us, among us, for us,
True democracy. Farewell.'

Then Nwoye Akubue said,
'Farewell, free bird of the same breeder's stock.

Good fortunes attend the merry man.
What is achieved in five strokes with anger,
Is achieved in half a stroke with smiles.
The fire may not burn in a hurry
That does not wish to die in a hurry.
The patient mind outlives the overreaching mind.
Whatever you do, heed the fate
Of the obstinate fly who followed the corpse to its grave.

'Remember that liking what you do is
Always worse than doing what you like.
To a free bird,
A few moments of greatness is as nothing
Compared to a lifetime of happiness.
Those who avoid war are avoided by it.
The vindictive man who went to blow his nose,
Blew away his eyes from their sockets.
It is true that the greater of two eyes
Misfeeds the mouth,
Heed what voice you may, but heed that
By which you will attain the greatest happiness.
Whatever you do, though, be wary of marriage
And evolutionary mismatch.
I see no crime greater than to deprive women,
The joy of a good throb.'

'Shut up,' said Nwabuno,
'A drunk lover is the greatest evil.'

Ignoring Nwabuno, I asked Nwoye,
'Which free bird, the weaverbird
The heron or the eagle?
Should birds not fly according to
The size of their wings?'

'Son, a class is most dangerous
For an open mind.
We should be what we must be

To maximize our freedom
At every class contact.'

'A man who stands for nothing falls for everything
But Nwoye, what then is a class?'

'A social class is that contained
In an open ball of truth in constant flux,
And they are members of that class
Whose normative behavior falls
Within the ball's radius,
Anchored to its central tenets -
The center of the class.
A class may be characterized
By its norm in a cultural state space.'

'Oh ho,' interrupted Nwabuno,
'Genius that was constantly
Awash with palm wine.'

Again, ignoring Nwabuno, I asked Nwoye,
'What is truth again?'

'Truth is a sociological phenomenon
Insufficient in and of itself
And incapable of being absolutely justified.
Every man wears a garb of his own truth
That defines the man.'

'Oh ho,' said Nwabuno,
The only truth you knew
Was the milky fluid that bathed your palate.' [3]

Nwoye interjected, making no bones
Of the fact that he was unfaithful to her.
'Son, I still say that marriage
Is a necessary but dangerous institution.
A man who must be unfaithful, though,

Should seek out a woman with fat buttocks.'

'Son, the gathering place of monkeys
Is at the foot of the tree and
Of the squirrels, the head of the palm tree.
O free bird of the same breeder's stock,
On singing day, let us gather
At the tree with seven branches.'

'Nwoye, before you go,
What say you freedom is?'

'Son, freedom is the ability of
An individual with sufficient
Political and economical wherewithal
To be self-determining.
Freedom is that sense of moral purpose
That must be allowed to flourish in a moral milieu.
The just laws of a land
Are its moral soul and the just enforcement
Of the law is its moral corpus.
Together, they are necessary and sufficient to
Provide an environment that engenders freedom.

'Freedom is not the mere absence of
Institutionalized repression.
It is a mindset that truly recognizes
That all men, being equal, are subject to
The same sensitivities.'

'Oh ho,' said Nwabuno,
'I knew there was something about you
That palm wine withheld from me.
Nwoye, you sought freedom in the gourd
And ruined our marriage.'

'Son, as universal as a palm kernel eater
Is this disposition of all women,

That they tend to be discourteous
When there are no yams in their husband's barn.
A wife's emotional abuse of her husband
Always precedes his physical abuse of her.[4]
Often people forget that the mouth cuts the soul;
The knife, the flesh.'

Nwabuno replied angrily,
'Nwoye, you were the eleemosynary of all time.
An indolent fool blames the dry spell,
Hunger soon uncovers him.
Trash talk is a companion to the trashy clad.
The truth, Nwoye, is that an old eagle does not soar.
You are the lizard, and palm wine, the insect
That would not last long on your tongue.'

Nwoye said,
'Son, of all men who took their lives seriously,
None escaped your world with it.
In this, they are no better than the rest of us
Who shunned the meters of shallow order and morality.'

Nwoye continued,
'Son, about the conduct of women,
I am the lion, who no matter how old it gets
Would always be adept at catching a goat.
And I tell you this,
That every woman is a wayward palm tree,
They know for whom their fruits fall.

'Son, is there love's intensity
Like that of a woman scorned?
She loves forever, when treated
With a little scorn, a little
Forced anger, and a pulse of pandering
And forever lasts a marriage.

'Should you ever get married
Bear in mind the analogy of
The couples and the cup.
There were the stupid couples who
Simultaneously drank from the same side
Of a cup, they spilled much and drank some.
Then, there were others who drank
Simultaneously from the opposite sides of the cup,
And neither could get a drink.
Then, there were the wise couples who took turns
At the cup, and life was fair to them.

'Son, be not so much in love as to lose
Your individuality. Our men made out houses
For their women and marriage prospered.
Men of your time have lost their guts.
They kiss too much and admit too much
Theories of misguided equalities.
Consequently, marriage has faltered.

'Son, a man worth his salt
Learns to ignore the acid bath of a woman's mouth.
It is better to live in the desert
Than to live with a foul-mouthed woman.
A man who openly declares
His love for a woman must
Pander to her undulating emotions.
For which is better: to wake up
With the most certain sure of
The salubrity of a well-tapped palm wine
Or a woman who might have grown fangs overnight?
Seek out a woman when she purrs
Like a cat, desiring attention
And the harmony of a drum
When the beast in her is declared.

'Son, I sought security in the gourd
After I lost patience with

The vicissitudes of a woman's ways.
Nwabuno of the slippery tongue,
To have married you at all
Is to have scaled the heights of greatness.
Who will blame Nwoye,
When men hear your voice?
Genius of the oral form,
A free bird's pride is the vast expanse
Of openly navigable space.
The words of your mouth encumbered me
And I sought freedom.[5]
I determined freedom and happiness
And I found them in the gourd
And the rhythms of a well-crafted drum.
The drums of Okweigba, of Awato,
Have as yet produced the most
Unsurpassable sounds.

'Nwabuno of the slippery tongue,
Should a man swallow phlegm
Because he is self-conscious about spitting it out?
Where fortune swings so sways a man's heart.
The fortunes of palm wine were
Greater than those of our conjugality,
And my heart swung.

'Son, one more thing,
Men of your time spend too much time
Clutching their testicles.
Has no one heard that the only thing
Worthy to hold in the mouth is the tongue?'

'Nwoye,' I replied, 'as far as that goes,
All I can say is that it is difficult
To avert from the pleasurable.
Just know that grains are no strangers
To the dove.'

'Son, tomorrow is another merry day
On the tree with seven branches
We will as yet sing our songs,
Unregulated, omnithematic
Songs of the free.'

Drumbeat! Drumbeat!

Then turning to Nwabuno I said,
'Farewell Nwabuno, beautiful fire
That cannot be held.
Verbal athlete, princess of the oral genre,
Soon, the world will bask in your orality.
When the stars constellate
To determine the joy of uncontrollable
Laughter, this fairy story
Shall have been told.

'Slowly, the stormy cloud gathers,
And the fear of deluge dampens our hearts.
When survivors recount
The tales of Armageddon
And the hurdled orphans of war
Partake of a subdued rejoicing,
At the crata's edge,
On the day of new lights,
At the eve of fresh sprouts of renewal,
After the seven eruptions,
We shall meet to celebrate
Our storied lives, and
Make apocalyptic songs of the path
Of blood, of the dearth of conscientious
Men at creation's dusk; and play
Out more inspirations of the oral form,
Long aspersed by the scribbly type.'

Then Nwabuno said,
'Farewell son of Ezenwanmadu,

The snake that assumes it is a lizard,
Falls off the wall with ignominy.
Self-negation is an existence crime.
Although occasional self-flagellation
And self-denial may bring one
To the crowning point of self-awareness,
In all things, you must know yourself
And be yourself that you know,
And assemble your conducts from
The vantage point of the self-embraced.'

Drumbeat! Drumbeat!

Then turning to them, I said,
'Now, I know why it is said
That an elderly pair of eyes is needed
To sort out an old and abandoned trail.
Thank you, O mystery fellows,
The ear rests that has heard.

'The blind man's stick is his light
With that he shatters darkness.
Even as a walking stick to the blind,
And as a climbing rope to the climber,
So have you been to me.

'Goodbye, O seminals of the human race.
A child's well spring of gratitude
Will always rise to salute
His mother's tender care.'

And Ezenwanmadu said,
'The snake does not strike a child
Before its mother.
A woman's tender care will not
Cease towards the child she bore.'

Drumbeat! Drumbeat!

'We *plant joy on the soil of thankfulness.*
We *do not ask an Iroko tree to hide itself,*
Under *its ramparts, let others thrive.*
For *he who does nothing for others,*
Does *nothing for himself.'*

Endnotes

[1] A green leafy vegetable.

[2] Agubanze, son of Ezenwanmadu, the author's direct ancestor, was married to Ebenebe's daughter.

[3] Nwabuno just would not let Nwoye, her ex-husband, forget that she resented his addiction to palm wine.

[4] Nwoye is an old schooler. Half the time he masks his genius by jesting a lot. In this case he is prodding Nwabuno by saying that it is always the woman's fault if she ends up being physically abused.

[5] Apart from the stark incongruity of their personalities, it is easy to imagine that as married couples, Nwabuno resented Nwoye's care-free nature, and could in fact, have been verbally abusive.

Chapter 16

One More Song To Sing

Wisdom, have you made war man's destiny
And admit as good music,
The roar of dying men?
Yet with blurry eyes and rippling tears,
With compassion profound, sincerely felt,
Have we seen you on their burial day.
Such are you, a confounder of men.
You, for whom humility is your greater part,
And honesty your chief ally.

Okonkwo, who is also called Euhemerus,
Mentioned that an empty stomach
Covers the navel. It was then I realized
How long it had been.
It was clear that I had
Seen the mystery fellows for the last time.
But there was Euhemerus, the drummer
Who had been with me all this while
And needed to be sent on his way.

So turning to Euhemerus, I said:
'Euhemerus, a poet's mind is a gallery
Of images, processing and swirling in endless
Motion and poetry is the grafting of emotions
Unto thought, overtopped with mild paronomasia.

'Euhemerus, the poet sees in fragments
And writes in fragments, and
Only he knows the nature of his otherness.
In this he is no less mad than a lunatic,
Sane as sane in his exclusive domain.

'Euhemerus, songs are like books,
Of their making there is no end
And men of emotion are well served by both.

'Euhemerus, a well-written book
Is an enduring treasure.
When written with sensual innuendoes,
It serves the voyeurs in all of men.

'Euhemerus, many are the personalities
Of every great artist.
They live where their personalities lead,
In the depths of absurdities or in
The sublimity of the ethereal, their caviar,
They must be left to freely choose their themes
And make love, if they would, on the boughs

Of their own visions.
For good art transcends both
Beauty and authorship and holds
Forth utility as its quintessence.
That which it is for everybody both
Defines and justifies it, and yet
Only in the heart of its author
Has art the greatest hope of reward.

'Euhemerus, men sought our inspiration,
They wondered by which school and master,
They sought and found not our kin
In the tribes of the artists and the prophets.
Then they finally asked and we said,
'By him who must be feared,
Who cuts off the spirits of the princes,
Who is terrible to the kings of the earth.
He alone inspires verses and instills
Images in the minds of good men.
At night he instills verses into me
And at day he commands write,
And I write.'

'They charged us with blasphemy.
Ah! Blasphemy! Sigh!
When the harvesters come
Like well-accoutered thieves at night,
What will the watchman do?

'Euhemerus, we have told men
That the sun will die,
They looked and laughed
And made more errors,
Yet the sun will die.

'We told men of the errors of hatred,
They looked and laughed
And hated some more, still

The sun will die on account of men's hate.

'Euhemerus, we have given men a book of revelation
Sprinkled with the language of the streets,
To suit the grain of their palate,
And for their edification,
We wove many tangles with words.
Instead, men got tangled in our style,
Making empty thesis thereof,
And of our delivery, they lost its substance.

'Still, like the irksome mosquito
Importuning the innocent ear,
Must we not continually remind them
That hate is the foundation of
A fool's paradise and those who
Cling to wealth and hate are as
Clingers to the frills of smoke?'

'*All heads are good for fatigue,*
But we have one more song to sing,
One more streak of light,
One more yawn before
The heroes lose their poise in sleep.'

Drumbeat! Drumbeat!

'O time of the strange anatomy,
Clad in a motley of fortunes,
Shrouded in uncertainties
And sometimes eagerly to be despised,
Whose discontented voice ought be raised?
Although many beseech you,
None relates to you in confidence.
You are the sure and unruly hypocrite,
And I am your irreverent hostage poised in spite.

'O time that defeats all,
And kills all who would kill it,
Ambitions killed twice, patience afflicted
More than once, would you hand me
A bolt of thunder to announce
My homecoming. Heavy and sad,
Blinded by smoke from the thurible,
Another ritual of murder,
Another exequy, and a blister burns into another –
The calloused epidermis of our hopes.

'Docile, the rebel has lost his heart,
Has come a full circle,
Has arrived where once he hated,
And the reform is forever deferred.'

Drumbeat! Drumbeat!

'The light flickers and dies,
Darkness! Hope molts in self-renewal,
Neurotransmitters fluxing in hope's clumps
And its mood indulges its biochemicals.'

'The orphan will have a child.'

'Pain dies with the aging scar,
Time drifts away in hurried steps,
The refrains of horror have ended,
And the memories of war are blurred.'

'Hurrah! The orphan has found a life.'

'Time will restore what so proudly we held
For it folds not back upon itself.'

'This orphan will have a child. Hurrah!'

'A thousand losses
Yet we won.
Hurrah to mind over matter
To insubstance, over substance.

'Agony is to the vanquished,
To the victor, lights, moments,
The dance stage, jubilation,
A thousand losses, yet
Our well-practiced dance steps grow sharper,
Mocks! And the victor is dismayed.

'The victor came to us and said,
'Should the stage not be mine?'
At which we replied that
Great men are burnished by adversities
And not dissuaded by them.
Again, the victor is dismayed.
And our well-practiced dance steps
Grow more intense.'

'*Izakarika. Izakarika ha ha.*'

'We will run again.
We will magnify our achievements.
We will persist until victory
Is redefined and these races
Shall have been run.'

'*Izakarika!*'

Drumbeat! Drumbeat!

Being more reassured, I *said,*
'Hurrah! The days of thunder are over.
Thunder that struck the tree,
The tree that struck the elephant,
The elephant that struck the grass,

The grass that Whitman sang about.

'Hurrah! The retailers may now
Gather at the marketplace,
The tapsters may now push their wares,
Those who can interpret palm wine
And will live forever, gather around
The fresh and effervescing gourd.'

Drumbeat! Drumbeat!

'The child becomes an adult becomes a child,
The storehouses of souls depleted by birth
Is replenished by death,
The abandoned nest eventually falls to the wind
So everything changes in the soul of the unchangeable.'

'The poet is dead,
The poet's apocalypse lingers on.
The poet is dead,
There are no mourners in the house.
The poet is dead,
Only joyful tears will drop.
The poet is dead,
The bat has left its perching spot.
The poet is dead,
The cock crows,
The adulterer sneaks back in.
The poet is dead,
The raindrop has finally entered the river.
The poet is dead,
He says life is a mirage.

'Nwoye, the village bohemian
Shouted a premature hurrah!
'Hurrah,' he said, 'thunder has died.'
'Still, Nwoye, the poet's voice
Re-echoes with a lingering unease.

Thunder will thunder again,
Again the air will crack.
Can the voice of a million
Angry men, smother the sound of a male thunder?'

Drumbeat! Drumbeat!

'But *for the neck and its entrails,*
The head is deserving of rest.
A word does not get ugly in the mouth,
But outside that watery housing;
The spoken word, the heart that is seen.
Verse maker, how often does it happen
That a man who drinks his first cup of water
Assumes he will never thirst again?'

'All heads are good for fatigue,
But we have one more song to sing,
One more streak of light,
One more yawn before
The heroes lose their poise in sleep.'

'Word! Virtue of the verse maker,
Envoy of my thoughts,
Anchor of my genius gone wild,
Deep sustainer at sorrow's gate,
You must justify me.

'Often unspoken or unwritten
You form the matrix of my thoughts.
By you am I structured,
And all forms stem from you.
Formless, diverse, ever fluid,
Parsimonious; yet with tender generosity
You give value and content to every life.

'Were you not it
Without whom was made

Nothing that was made?
The way, the truth, you are the life.
First made, beginning of the beginning,
Inchoate, immanent, the creator's soul.
Omnific and deificable,
Immortal, limpid like a pond,
Reflecting the mysteries of life,
You must justify me.

'Side by side, bearing arms,
Comrades ever, we will wage
The war of understanding and
Toil by night as well as day,
Relentlessly scheming
Past my soul's bedtime.

'Mangled by the affected erudition
Of immoral men, we will hold on,
Protecting that sacred to us,
The knowledge that truth, never known,
Shall not be known, the only truth
That should calm a troubled soul,
Yet in whose pursuit and search
Our beings a purpose take,
And glorifying those assertions
By which we are most aroused,
And holding firm to a beleaguered
Sense of purpose, we form
A companionship of class and race, and lose
The fluidity by which we were meant
To flow, into, around and between
All forms, great and small.

'Today, we will no longer
Hunt for words
Or hunger after it.
We have dined enough
And belched of wine-laden breath.

We have hung and despaired together.
When all hope was lost, we wept.
Great was our sorrow,
Greater still our joy,
And great, the labors of our hearts.

'We have borne the lyncher's stick
And the strangler's rope,
And lamented death of love unborn.
Desperate, anxious, yet hopeful,
We have fled from mobs
Unappeased by our blood.
Fleeing from our assailants, we swam
In dung-infested waters
And breathed air, dank with body fluids.
Although at times we stepped aside
And engaged in mutual arousal,
And tickled each other's *erotogen*.

'We have knelt together,
On creased knees, bowed our heads,
Folded our hands, in solemn suppliance
We prayed, that our wills
May with the godhead's fuse.
But not without mercy,
Not without divine condescension
Would we breathe the breath of God,
And like a strong wind, mission bound,
Would we catalyze the chemistry of his works.

'Word, O faithful companion,
Blessed be our maker.
For your ever watchful guide
And your nudging encouragement,
I am thankful. You are the vehicle
By which they have been sorted out,
The nuances to which I am inclined and
Have glorified my profoundest thoughts

Unlocking my impassioned pleas,
You roused up my ebbing impetuosity,
You have truly justified me.

'Let my heart like drum beating
Not betray my trust in you.
For like a silent fate sustained
Is my hope of life to come
And our adventures together
Beyond the pale of this present life.'

Drumbeat! Drumbeat!

'We are both like the peripatetic antelope
How could we be anything but slender?
Where the light goes off, we break our journey.
Where darkness meets the itinerant medicine man,
He eats of his fees.'

'Euhemerus, was sleep not worth a trifle
In the days of our innocence?
Today, steeped in triste,
Our eyelids are emptied of her.
She has found a new consort
With the wind has she been seen
Everywhere, but with us.
O sleep, please come back
For with you are we born again.'

Drumbeat! Drumbeat!

'Euhemerus, the night has finally cast her pall.
Turn off the light, close the shutters,
The eyes, the soul's window to the world.
Let all traffic of human thoughts cease.
To the syncopation of nature's breath sleep.
Heave a sigh, long, drawn out, purgative,
Overlook the politician's chicanery,

Bury today's conflicts,
Tomorrow shall yield more.

'Let these shadows cast by the trees,
Let these shadowy outlines of nature's love
Adorn our quiescent minds.
Let go!
Swirl into the zone of frictionless energy.
Worry not about truth.
Something about her would never be known,
What shade she is,
Whereof her mother's land,
What stuff her mission,
Something about her,
Let truth inquire unto itself.

'In parting let our thoughts be thus:
Something about duality,
The two sides a coin must have.
When something stands,
There is always a *stander-by*.
Has Nwoye not taught that
Life and death, truth and falsity,
Good and bad, are a neumenological corpus,
Unitary, inseparable, and co-rationalized;
Life's contradictions breeding
Cauldron of conflicts.

'Every man is a collector
Of truths and falsities.
Hung over his back, his own
Baggage, his dignities and indignities.'

'Hush! Listen! Let go of over-worn thoughts.
Hush! The squirrels say one to another,
'Something about wisdom,
That robs men of their innocence.
Something about powerlessness,

Why men disdain it.
Why, when given the reins of power,
The erstwhile peasant becomes dictatorial.
Something about disorder,
Why men are discomfitured by it.
Something about infinite reality,
Why men are awed by it.
Infinity is nonexistent,
Why do men pretend to comprehend it?

'Something about nothing,
Why men are puzzled by it.
Something about the race of life,
Why the trampled and the trampler
Are both harried, yet is
The trampler deemed great
If he profits by it.

'Something about these puzzles
We may never know
As beyond our ken, they are.
But not to be eloigned
Is the matter of the kernel of
Buried nuts, that should form the kernel
Of our own philosophic inquisitions.

'Yet must it be added,
That those who do not talk
Do not lament the limitations of language.
Therein lies the greatness of the drum,
Throbbing, not talking,
Disseminating harmony.
Not even a breeder's display
Elicits so much excitement.

'Something about the world of humans
That should be left to them.
Say, upon which palm tree

Shall we make our sport tonight?'

Drumbeat! Drumbeat!

'A *child's wisdom is his parent's pride.*
Not like the anxiety of the parents of the glib
Child who told the spirits
That his mother's soup was not well spiced.
Brother, if I did not see the tortoise climb
The Iroko tree, I would have sworn that
Somebody put him up there.
It is indeed a pattern with our marvelous God
That he elects to make the rejected stone,
The corner stone.'

'Goodbye Euhemerus,
Our bodies have done this journey
That has done our bodies.
We have followed the past
Up to the extent that it goes
Only to come upon the present.
Now we know what the preacher knew,
That there is nothing that shall be
That has not been.
And futile are the efforts of strivers
Whom the present, its course, dare to steer.
For thus knowing we must now rest.
We must cast anchor on the waters of the past,
And berth in the shipyards of the present.
For when tomorrow a new tide comes,
We will set sail adrift that ordered reality,
Resigned to the urge to make a change.

'Is this not the principle of universal determinism?
Propounded and wrought into every fabric of matter
By none other than the Lord of men.
For in acting, the universe acts upon us.
Thus knowing, we will ignore arrogant men

Whose hands are bowed in utter ignorance.
For what use is there to squash an ant
Who assumes its mighty thighs trigger earthquakes?

'Euhemerus, as harmonious as the teeth and the tongue,
So have we been.
But our journey's end has finally reached us
Although our destination lies beyond us.
We have crossed seven seas and seven mountains
We are truly weary of trudging,
Yet our destiny lies beyond us.
We will come to the misty top
Of another mountain,
And lap up its thin air,
And look forward to the exhilaration
In the lush greenery of the valley,
And on and on we will go for time unending.

'We will sit still,
Look at the distance,
And admire time's inrolling fog
Drifting toward and by us.
We will let the smiling facade
Of the onrushing cloud
Greet our upcast face,
And behold nature in all
Its munificence, and muse upon
The *primevality* of the mountain top,
And upon the errors of those
Who have pitted themselves against her,
In accordance with beliefs
Borne out of gain search.

'We will not be tied to time,
For time, insubstantial, vanishes,
But we will endure for all time.
For time envelops us,
Lacking in consistency, fleeting ever,

We will not join hands adrift with her.
However, let our utterances beautify
The times that sail past us.
Let our good deeds like festoons dropping,
Be a testimony that we were bathed by it.

'Idling by the river,
Stretched out along,
We will let the river flow,
And neither interpret nor
Apply any more doctrines.
For the problem with our human world
Is the conflict of interpretations,
And fundamental attitudinal differences,
Not dearth of doctrines.

We will salute each
Returning packet of water.
With each particle of it,
We will associate an idle thought.
So that arm linked,
Evaporating, condensing,
And molecularizing in tandem,
Our idle thoughts will
Suffuse all of matter.

'Sweet river of joy supreme,
Sweet river of predestined course,
Issuing from an inexhaustible store house,
Fixated transients, eternal paradox
Of creation, watery agents of the gods,
Be you our thoughts.

'And if any lines should come
Strolling into our heads,
We will bid it the river to swim,
Drenching it in the echoes of creation.

'There on the mountain top,
We will for once ignore
The hypocrisy of tyrannical Christians,
The utter privation of Buddhist monks,
The furious menace of
Fundamentalist Islamic religiosity,
The ungodly exclusivism of people of the book,
The tawdry of diviners and star gazers,
The tedious incantations of spiritists and evil worshipers,
And breathe an air of solace
From all that fury and fray,
And from men whose interest
Run narrow and deep.
Heaven seekers, who know not
The joy of the mountain top,
Men thrilled by hate, how can
The boundless heavens welcome you
That are bounded by creeds
And sects and dusty cants?

We will decry the dictatorship of wealth,
And the politicization of abjurative sciences,
And doctrines of war,
Upon which the thinker's mind is spilled,
About which verses would be to dignify
Men of eloquence temporarily thrust
To the top, ideological criss -crossers
Motivated by self interest, sanguinary
Oppressors and hypocrites of the ruling clique…

'There we will vehemently denounce
Voluble silence, predator
Of the revolutionary's heart,
Idle revolutionaries, breathless men
Prone to self-annihilation,
Vapid ideologues,
Compulsive free loaders,
Stay-at-homers, skilled

In gathering the spoils of war,
Renegades, shifters with the wind,
Political drifters, cult mongers
Who claim unbestowed greatness,
Iron-willed, most sagacious
Ever victorious, self-deluding
Socialist dictators,
Liars and hate mongers
Like immodest death trampling,
Arm twisters, violent men
Of every ilk and plume,
Fascists who affect good manners,
Gradualists who peddle sophistry,
Freedom without love,
Tempered by the insouciance
Of the middle class,
Men who preach peace
To their mother's assailant,
Horde of disparagers,
Snoopers and tale hunters,
Delirious reporters
Who hasten to tell a lie,
Pledgors to needless causes,
Misguided activists, shoguns,
Doctrinaires of slave accommodation;
Deliberate extinctioners of democratic zeal,
Neocons, lips parted in mockery
Of a world without conflicts…
Men who eat lizards and dine upon their eggs.

'Unabashed, rustic,
By that undisciplined etiquette
Of pure animalism,
We will assert in what form or manner we deign,
So that bereft of literary finish
And florid word stippling
We will preach on.
For it matters not to us

Which way the wind blows,
We will sail on.
We will not adopt any style or creed,
Of imitation, we will beware
Night and day, and even if
Profit comes by it,
We will be weary still.

'Minds of men and all
Incarcerated minds wheresoever born,
Is this not the urger's song?
A cordial of visionary songs,
A pabulum to sustain all clenched fists
So that you may break loose
And justify me, black salt, no less tasty,
Pungent to the critic's taste, stimulant,
Disperser of all that is pallid,
Seasoner of all that I season,
I, he that urges, step ahead,
Alone without me, your rear guard,
Cheerful, dead or alive, at freedom's mansion,
Against the sun thrust,
Ostentatious rendezvous,
The end, where I must be justified.

'Euhemerus, Go now,
I hear the drum major
Who urges me to dream on.
I hear the barrel laugher
Who makes light my burden.

'Go now,
The words of the old Negro spirituals
Are ringing all around me:
'We trod upon a road, so stony,
And bitter, the rod with which
Our God chastised us,
When the hope for which we yawned,

Died before its birth.'
The barrel laugher stifled a laughter.
Solemn is this moment,
More so, than on the eve of a mother's death.

'Go now,
Songs are stuck in my throat
And they compel me.
Indifferent to harmony or gruff,
To all that is aesthetic and delightful,
The symbolic deflectors from life's true path,
And before the shimmering noonday sun,
Before my coevals, the planets and the stars,
Ill clad like the slave,
With bruised hands upraised,
My equal significance, I proclaim,
With all that was ever made.
We were conceived, the universe and I,
Contemporaneously, in the same breeder's womb.

'Go now Euhemerus, for a while
Then another while, and half a while,
We will meet again to see
How spring has affected the withered plants.'

Drumbeat! Drumbeat!

After this, Euhemerus, sad
And overcome by emotion, said,
'Wisdom, have you made war man's destiny
And admit as good music,
The roar of dying men?
Yet with blurry eyes and rippling tears,
With compassion profound, sincerely felt,
Have we seen you on their burial day.
Such are you, a confounder of men.
You, for whom humility is your greater part,
And honesty your chief ally.

You who has taught that
Not in life is there peace,
Nor is such the fruit of death,
The earth being not such that
Men may attain happiness in it,
Or that war be no part of it,
But that it be ruled by the will of God;
That being that men being wise may
Learn to despise all temporal gains.'

Then I said in parting,
'Euhemerus, happiness is not always an alien
At sorrow's gate. Our joy is magnified today.
A mother may masticate for her baby
But she will never swallow for it.
All these people of many nations
Whom we have nudged uphill
Have also gotten us closer to the top
And in their honor and joy,
We will truly be honored.

'What then should we say to them
Whom we have this far brought?
For together we have partaken
Of their mind's afforestation…

'Should we say,
If you own a skunk, cut its mouth,
If you own a toad, open its belly,
For when a house falls,
Its festoons fall as well?

'Should we say,
Let him who must learn about burrows
Seek out the grass cutters,
For a woodpecker knows the tree
That bears the bitter sap, ask it,
Inquire not of the climbers of the land,

Inquire not even of Izaka to scorn,
Is man not the proper study of mankind?

'Should we say,
A giraffe is accustomed to great strides,
Look to the giraffe, not to Izaka,
Not to the human race search,
For markers so ill defined?

'Whatever we say, let one thing
Above all be said,
That the embracement of wisdom
Is the beginning of ignorance,
And many are those who strain
Their minds in vain.
Yet wisdom is a blessing
If men show it not,
That men may in all things
Be true to men.'

Drumbeat! Drumbeat!

'*Wisdom is a hilly landscape,*
Only a fool struts unaided.
The boastful wise man
May be asked to distinguish
One ant from another.'

'Farewell, son of Ezenwanmadu,
A clear conscience is the pillow
Upon which good men lay their heads.
Now is as good as any to sleep
Or we could remain awake,
If we must wait for that perfect sleep
That goes through the nostrils.'

So saying, the drumbeat faded.
Euhemerus had gone to rejoin his kinsmen.

I sat up, morose and overwhelmed.
I wiped the corners of my eyes
And promptly knelt down
As I had become accustomed to doing
For I knew by whose friendship I had enjoyed
The visitation of the mystery fellows.
I turned inward and said:

'Silently, my gracious lady waits for me.
May only time embellish this tribute
To be rendered as eloquently as my pen could.
From where my head is tilted,
I have felt your anointing oil flow merrily.
For out of the syrup of your goodness
Have arisen such profound impulses,
Such alignment with divinity, such eager acceptation,
Such beneficiation, such actuation …
And once again, have you death destroyed.

'O God of my fathers,
In a quarter of a lifetime,
You have instilled in me
The pain of a million lifetimes.
Enormous is my profound anguish,
Melancholy besets me,
Your love stirs sorrow in me,
And anger and zeal sometimes consume me,
For I have seen that the preferred disposition of men
Is evil, hatred and arrogance
By which you uproot them,
And further by their stubbornness,
You let then wither like uprooted stumps.

'Still, mired in misery,
Your beauty comes flowing to me,
And again and again, I say,
'Wonderful are your works,
In wisdom you conduct your affairs.'

'O Lord, of all burdens,
There is none greater than the knowledge of your ways,
Yet it is in such a burden that my yoke is lifted,
For all that you taught me burned into me
And my agony multiplied,
Until I sought relief from the burden of wisdom
Whereupon you said, 'Son, lean not on thy wisdom.'
And so, relieved and blissful in my foolishness,
I recite with heart all content that I too
Know that I do not know.

'I know that I could never know.
I know that you are all there is to know.
Thus have you, seated in righteousness,
Allotted confusion to men.
By likening you to ourselves,
Men have held to your wrongful attribution,
The sins of hate, uncertainty and insecurity
And have set as true doctrines, the precepts of men.
But you are the one, universal,
Immanent, transcendent being,
Whose bountifulness extends indiscriminately
To creatures of all ages,
To men of all races,
And to beings of all likenesses.

'As your inerrable will disposes
Have you made an imperfect man
And his imperfect world,
Perfectly to your will.
By observing your reflection
In every station and in every facet
Of creation, have I perceived,
A unitariness in your being.
And that is, that the core consciousness
In all beings, spiritual and temporal,
May, after carrying out their assigned roles,
Return to their source, which is you.

'For the purposes of your divine instruction,
Have you created a full spectrum of circumstances.
To one you have caused to be born black,
To another, white.
To one you have caused to be born into slavery,
To another, into a king's household.
To one you have caused to be born into Islam,
To another, Christianity.
To one you have assigned an early death,
To another, longevity.
To one you have assigned foolishness,
To another, wisdom.

'Hear then, O Lord, my God,
The prayers of all your children
Whom you have spread over all the earth,
Which by your divine grace
I bring in supplication before your holy presence.
In your mercy, unite all mankind,
Wherever you have put them.
Restore in mankind a hunger for righteousness,
And a fervent desire to seek your ways.
Avert your eyes from our acts of wickedness,
So that your anger may not overtake us,
And grant us that peace which accompanies
Spiritual progress.

'By this one thing, and only this, shall I have gained,
And in it lies all the reward I seek,
That a single line of verse may make another
Rethink their arrogance in relating to you,
And to their fellow beings,
For then all glory shall have been yours,
You, the fountain of all goodness,
And in your glory shall my recompense be.

'How risible, very risible indeed,
That men measure their worth in gold,

And account of selves as good,
When you benignly turn away.'

'And so, with this, be you buried,
A phase, littered with men of utmost contumely,
And led by hearts inclined to ignorance,
To arrogate the proper manners of God.

Give the gift of
Do Not Let Us Die
to your friends and colleagues

Check your local bookstore, visit www.DoubleCrest.com or www.Amazon.com, or order below.

YES Send me _____ copies of Do Not Let Us Die for $24.95 each. I've included $3.95 shipping and handling for one book, and $1.95 for each additional book. (**Maryland** residents must include 5% sales tax. **Canadian orders** must include payment in US funds, with 7% GST added.)

Payment must accompany orders. Allow 3 weeks for delivery.

☐   My check or money order for $_____ is enclosed.

☐   Please charge my ☐Visa ☐MasterCard ☐AmEx

Name _____

Organization _____

Address _____

City/State/Zip _____

Daytime Phone _____

E-mail _____

Card # _____

Exp. Date _____   Signature _____

Make your check payable and MAIL to:
DoubleCrest Publishers, LLC
P.O. Box 2340, Bowie, MD, 20718

Or FAX your order to: (301) 352-3251
www. DoubleCrest.com
Email: Publisher@DoubleCrest.com
Call: (301) 352-2424